ADVENTURES IN RELIGION

BOOKS BY

BASIL KING

ADVENTURES IN RELIGION

BY BASIL KING

DOUBLEDAY, DORAN & COMPANY, INC.

GARDEN CITY   1929   NEW YORK

CONTENTS

CHAPTER I

WHAT IS RELIGION?

LEROY was well into his thirties before he began to take any interest whatever in religion. Even then his interest was less in religion than it was in his children. It seemed absurd that between their mother and himself they could not teach them anything. Bobby was twelve; Ellie nearly eight. At their ages he himself had known a lot about the Bible, fragments of what they called a catechism, a number of hymns, and his prayers. At Ellie's age he had said his prayers, digging his elbows into his father's or his mother's knees, while he writhed in contortions calling down blessings on uncles, aunts, and friends. At Bobby's age he said them by himself, kneeling sedately at his bedside. But these children never said a prayer. They didn't know any. Neither Mabel nor he had

1

ever taught them. Mabel had grown up in a family that had no religion, and he had abandoned his during his second year at Harvard. But between his wife and himself there was this difference, that Mabel never having known the practice felt no remorse, whereas he was conscious of a vague discomfort like that of the wound he had got at Belleau Wood, which, though long ago healed, started up every now and then to ache again.

The worst of it was that their house was opposite a church. It was a church with a large congregation who were not satisfied with services on Sunday but spilled over into weekdays. The children would stand at the windows watching the people, among whom were boys and girls no older than themselves, trooping in and out. Sooner or later the young lookers-on would be asking what it meant.

And one day Ellie did. "Mother, is that a picture theatre?" "No, dear; it's a church." "What's a church?" "It's a place where people go to practise their religion." It was Bobby who asked the next question, doing it in a tone which implied that he had often been puzzled by the subject. "Mother, what's religion?" "Go and ask your father, dear. He'll explain to you."

They were all three in the front drawing room which looked toward the church. He was in the back drawing room, reading the evening paper before going to his room to dress for dinner. Bobby came straight to his father's knee. A tall boy, with handsome, intelligent features, a set mouth, a clean-cut nose, and truthful eyes that still shone with the clouds of glory which he had come trailing, it was no wonder that Leroy adored him.

"Father, what's religion?"

Leroy pretended to be still reading his paper. "You wouldn't understand, son, if I were to tell you."

It was the reply that children most resent. "I know I could understand if you'd explain to me."

Slightly ashamed, the father let his paper drop. "I know you could, old boy, but I can't explain because I don't know very well my-

self. But this is what I'll do. I'll think it over
and try to tell you this time to-morrow."

"All right, Father. That's a promise, and I'll
ask you then."

A good part of the night Leroy lay awake
trying to find the definition that would satisfy
the boy. Little by little he came to see that it
must also be one that would satisfy himself.
"What the dickens is it?" he kept repeating, as
he tossed from side to side. "I know in a way;
and yet in a way I don't know."

He went back to the religious impressions of
his early years and found that they did not help
him much because they were all in confusion.
His father had been brought up a Methodist,
but as Leroy remembered him he wasn't anything. His mother, on the other hand, had been
an ardent Episcopalian—an Anglican she preferred to call herself—and had tried to make
another of her son. To this the father presented
only the objection of a secret derision, and yet
a derision not so secret but that the boy easily
divined it. Outwardly, he did as his mother
told him. He went to church! he was con-

firmed; he received the Holy Communion. But he too maintained a form of secret derision in order to be like his father.

When he was sixteen his father died, leaving him to the guardianship of his mother, though the trustee of his fortune was his Uncle Charlie, his father's brother, who was also to be his guardian in case of his mother's death before he came of age. Like his father, his Uncle Charlie had been brought up a Methodist, but having in his youth fallen desperately in love with a pretty Irish girl, the daughter of a wealthy contractor and politician, he had conformed to the Roman Catholic faith because there had been no other way of getting her.

A year after his father's death his mother was stricken with a mortal complaint. Never should he forget the day when she told him she had only another six months to live. "I've talked to your Uncle Charlie and your Aunt Agnes," she had added, "and they've promised me they'll never interfere with your religion."

This promise they kept faithfully. During the three years he had made his home with them—though most of the time he was at college—no attempt to "convert" him was ever made by anyone. True, with his cousins, of whom there were four, he often had disputes as to the part Anne Boleyn had played in the founding of his Church; but these rarely went beyond a "She did not," on his part, and "She did too," on theirs. Into his uncle, in spite of his conformity, he read the same secret derision he had recognized in his father, while Aunt Agnes never went beyond a gentle refusal to recognize in his Church any ground in common with her own. "We have an Apostles' Creed just like yours in our Church," he had once ventured to assert. "Oh, but it's not the same thing," Aunt Agnes had declared readily. "We've got a Virgin Mary in our Church, too," had been another of his claims. "Oh, but it's not the same thing," she had retorted. A third declaration of faith had taken the form of, "We believe in the Trinity just the same as you do," to which Aunt Agnes had come back with, "Oh, but it's not the same thing at all."

He liked his Aunt Agnes. In as far as any-

one could take his mother's place she had done
it. But the effect of her quiet and repeated nega-
tions was to introduce into religion an element
of contradiction to itself which made it easy
for him to give it up. This he did not do finally
till his second year at Harvard. In his first
year he simply didn't practise it, but by his
second he had been thrown with a group of
fellows whose profound scientific knowledge
led them to abandon the whole thing. What
they couldn't see with their eyes, touch with
their fingers, and taste with their palates, it
was no use asking them to believe. Leroy's
secret derision came out into the open, and
stayed in the open, till he himself was in the
Château-Thierry salient. What he felt about
religion then was the vague regret he experi-
enced when he thought of something which
would have been useful to him there, had he
not left it behind.

That was as far as he had ever gone till
lately. Lately he began to see that the boy was
growing up. While, like other children, he was
always asking questions difficult to answer,

yet within a year his questions had grown so
reasonable that it seemed criminal not to give
them reasonable answers. Differing from what
was supposed to be the rule, Leroy was more
drawn to his little son than to his little daughter. Not that he loved him more, but he understood him better. Girls and women he frankly
didn't understand at all; men and boys, because
of their relative lack of complexity, were as
an open book to him. He knew about this boy
because he knew about himself, and for that
reason also he yearned over him. Girls he
thought of as sheltered; a boy had to face so
much. This lad, for whose safety he longed as
he had never longed for anything for himself,
would be exposed to the temptations which
each generation took in turn. If religion could
give him any help Leroy was anxious that he
should have it.

Next day at the office was a busy one, and
only now and then could he snatch a thought
for the subject Bobby had raised. When he did
he saw rows of churches, all mutually hostile.
Aunt Agnes's voice came back to him: "Oh,

but it's not the same thing." Each church apparently had its own Apostles' Creed, its own Virgin Mary, its own Trinity, of which it had a monopoly. As far as he had ever understood it shared nothing with any other. This seemed to be understood by a few words he had with Simpkins, one of the older partners.

"Say, Simpkins, can you give me a definition of religion?"

Simpkins, who was passing, looked at him in dull wonder. "You're an Episcopal, aren't you?"

"Nominally—yes—I suppose."

"Well, I'm a Baptist. Why don't you ask someone of your own kind?"

"Because a Baptist definition of religion would be good enough if it was only simple."

"Oh, hang!" Simpkins returned briefly. "Ask me something easier."

Simpkins having gone on his way, Leroy was driven to take a perfectly frank course with his little boy, who came to him that evening to keep him to his promise. "No, I haven't forgotten, old chap, but I've not got the answer yet. I'm thinking it over. Before I tell you I want to get it straight with myself, and when I do we'll go into the whole thing. Will that do?"

The boy said it would do quite well, and his being content to give his father time relieved Leroy of the necessity of making a bungling, insincere reply. But he thought the more. He thought so much that it became like an obsession. At the end of a week he felt like going to some clergyman, and only refrained because he didn't know one.

Then at the club he found himself sitting near a window close to Bowes, the journalist, whom he considered a good friend. Each was turning the pages of a current magazine. Leroy sprang his question without previous intention.

"Say, Bowes, what's religion?"

Bowes was as much astonished as Simpkins had been. "Why do you ask me?"

"I want an answer that will satisfy the kid. He's been putting the question up to me, and I don't know what to say."

"Look it up in the dictionary. That's what I

always do when my youngsters come bothering me."

No sooner said than done. There was a dictionary in eight or ten volumes just across the room. Within a minute Leroy had the great tome open on his knees.

At first he seemed not to get much light. He learned that from very ancient times the root meaning of the word had been in dispute. Cicero and others of his era had seen it as related to *religens,* which meant "reverent," while Servius, Lactantius, and St. Augustine, together with most moderns, derived the word from *re,* "back," and *ligare,* "to bind." That meant to bind back, to bind tightly, in such a way as to make a bond between one being and another. If that were so then religion was what bound man to God, and God to man, in a unity from which there could be no escape. Feeling that he had received as much as his mind could turn over at one time, Leroy shut the big book and carried it to its place.

His first impulse was to tell the boy that evening, but on second thoughts he saw that for his own sake this would be too soon. If he were to speak of a tie between man and God Bobby's next question would be as to who was God. Were he to tell him that God was "up in heaven," as people so often said to children, he would then have to meet the embarrassing query, "Where is heaven?" Now that he was tackling the subject at all there was one point on which he was resolved, to say nothing to the boy which would not be truthful as far as he himself could apprehend the truth. This might not be very far, but it would be the best that he could do. Should he attempt to speak on mere hearsay, or on the strength of what other people knew, he was sure those honest eyes would convict him of insincerity before he had said twenty words.

He must therefore find out what he thought himself, and to do that he must think. But thinking was easier now since he had a basis for thinking on. "To bind; to bind back; to bind tightly; to recognize a tie, an obligation." It interested him to perceive in that word "obligation" a syllable in common with the word "re-

ligion." Somewhere far, far back in the prehistoric, before there was a written language
to record the fact, men had been busy with
exactly the same problems as those with which
he himself was wrestling, and had twisted their
uncouth primitive sounds to form new words
to express new shades of meaning. Before
Latin had become the strong, terse vehicle for
thought which Virgil and Horace found it,
perhaps before the Roman had accepted the
dialect of Latium as his mother tongue, *re-
ligare* and *ob-ligare* had been coined to denote
ideas akin and yet apart. They were still apart,
and yet they were still akin, and it helped to
clarify his mind to see the association. The
binding together created an obligation on the
one side and on the other. It did not merely
involve man; it involved God. Religion was
not all supremacy for God and all abasement
on the part of man; it was a condition of in-
terdependent interests, like those of parent and
child or husband and wife. Where God was
the Father and Man was the Son, and the same

Holy Spirit proceeded from them both, the Unity and Trinity must be indissoluble.

Reasoning like this, he seemed to work his way behind the churches which bewildered him, reaching the source from which they all sprang. It was not through them that he came to the Father; it was through the Father that he came to them. The tie was not primarily between himself and them; it was primarily between himself and God. The religion that *bound* was a personal thing. That made it simpler, easier to grasp. It was also easier to take it basically, when he came to the point of explaining to the boy.

For at last a day had come when he felt qualified to speak, if only with hesitation. It chanced to be an afternoon when Mabel was out late and Ellie somewhere with her governess. This left them the back drawing room to themselves, with no one to overhear them.

"Do you remember that a few weeks ago you asked me what religion was?"

Bobby came and nestled against his shoulder. "Yes, Father. Do you know now?"

"I know better than I did then; but it's very hard to talk about."

"Why is it hard to talk about?"

"Because there are things for which language doesn't give us the right words. They're generally things that we can know well enough in our minds and hearts, and yet there's hardly any way of expressing them. I'll give you an example. I'm your father; you're my little boy. There's nothing I wouldn't do for you, and there's nothing you wouldn't do for me. And yet if I asked you to tell me why you'd find it hard to say."

"No, I shouldn't. It's because we love each other."

"Yes, that's part of it; perhaps it's nearly all of it; but there's still something which it doesn't tell us. There's duty, for example, and there's mutual interest, and there's nature, and almost every other good thing that exists. They all work together to make a bond between us. Do you understand?"

"I understand some of it."

"Well, then, it's very difficult to say anything

about that bond further than that it is a bond. You *know* what it is, and *I* know what it is; but we can't find words for it. We can feel it; we can *live* it; we can do all kinds of things because of it; but when it comes to telling anybody else exactly what it is, well, we just don't know how."

"But is that religion?"

"I think it's more like religion than anything else that we have in our ordinary life, because God . . ."

Searching for words he hesitated long enough for the boy to come in with a question which apparently seemed to have troubled him for years. "Well, now, Father, who's God?"

Having expected this, Leroy had already thought out his answer. "The best way we have of understanding who God is is to think of Him as being to all the world something like what I am to you. He'd be a great deal better than that, of course. I've got faults——"

The boy was indignant. "No, you haven't, Father."

"Well, then, let's suppose I haven't. Let's

suppose I'm perfect. Still I'm only your father and Ellie's. But God is the Father of all the people in the world. Religion is the relation in which I stand to Him. It's also the relation in which He stands to me. It isn't anything we think out, not any more than your being my son is something you think out. Just as that's a condition into which you were born, so religion is a condition into which everyone is born. In the same way, just as you can't choose whether you'll be my son or not, so we can't choose whether we'll be the sons of God or not. We're born into the relationship. Do you see?"

Bobby answered slowly, "I think I do."

"What's open to you is not to take any notice of the relationship; not to take any notice of me; to ignore me; to forget me. But even if you did you'd be my son just the same, wouldn't you?"

"Yes, of course."

"Well, that's what a great many people do toward the Father whom we call God. They say they haven't got such a Father. Or if they admit they've got such a Father they don't pay

Him any attention. They think they'll escape the bond by forgetting all about it. But they can't. They're born to it. It's a state of being. It's part of being born a member of the human race. Now that's the first thing I want to say."

"And what's the second?"

"The second has to do with the word 're-legion.' You know that all words have their histories. The very simplest we use come to us from other words, and they from other words, away back into the time when human beings first began to speak. For example, I read the other day that our word 'horse' comes from the Sanskrit word *as* which means 'swift.' Sanskrit is one of the most ancient languages we know anything about, and used to be spoken in Asia. But the word that meant 'swift' passed through a lot of other languages before it came to us, and by that time it had become 'horse.' Another illustration is our word 'stranger.' What do you think that comes from?"

Bobby, all eagerness, said he didn't know.

"It comes from the little Latin word *ex,* which isn't a bit like it, and means 'out of.'

But when the Roman wanted to speak of an outsider he called him *extraneus;* and when the Frenchman tried to say *extraneus* he made it —what? How does Mademoiselle say stranger?"

"*Étranger.*"

"Exactly, and when the people who first spoke English tried to say *étranger* they turned it into 'stranger.' Well, all words have a history more or less like that, and the word 'religion' has its own. How many syllables has it got?"

The boy counted slowly. "Three."

"Yes, it has three, and the important one is the middle one. How do you spell that?"

He replied correctly: "L-i-g."

"That's right; and now I'm going to say something which I hope you'll remember all your life. But first I want to ask you if you know what a ligament is?"

"It's something you've got in your leg, isn't it?"

"Yes, you've got it in your leg, and in your arm, and all over your body. A ligament is the strong fibre that binds the little bones together and helps them to act as one. And that word has a syllable in common with the word religion, hasn't it?"

"Why, yes; l-i-g."

"Well, there you get the vital meaning of the word. That l-i-g comes to us directly from the Latin word *ligo,* 'I bind.' But thousands and thousands of years ago there must have been people who first got hold of the syllable and made it mean what afterward it did. You might say that ligaments are what bind the body together so that it can act as one body. In the same way religion is what binds God and Man together so that they can act as one, and that then it is what binds all the human race together so that *it* can act as one."

The innocent eyes opened wide. "And does it?"

"It does it as an ideal. Do you know what an ideal is?"

"Isn't it something—" he sought for words —"awfully nice?"

"It's something awfully nice that we see with our inward eyes and have not as yet worked out.

We know it's what we ought to work out—but as yet we don't know how. For instance, you said the other day that you wanted to speak French as well as Mademoiselle, but that it would take you a long time. Well, that's your ideal. You can't do it yet; but you try and try, and one day you'll succeed. In the same way the human race has a great many ideals that it hasn't worked out this year, but that it will work out some other year. It may take a good many years——"

"How many? Ten?"

"In what we're talking about it will more likely take ten hundred or ten thousand—we can't say at all. But sooner or later we'll do it. The better we understand what religion is the more we'll see it as the bond which binds us all together. First it will have to bind together all the people in one church; then all the people of one country; then all the people who call themselves Christians. But we can't stop there. We shall have to understand that the people who are not Christians have their religions too, and while we think the Christian is the best we must see them as trying to do with theirs what we're trying to do with ours. Just as there's only one God——"

"Have we got the same God as—as Chinamen?"

"That's not the way to put it. There's only one God, and we see Him in one way, and the Chinaman in another, and the Hindoo in another, and the Turk in another, and the Hebrew in another, because none of us as yet knows very much about Him. Even among ourselves we don't all see Him in exactly the same way. The Catholic doesn't see God as the Protestant does, and the different kinds of Protestants don't see Him all alike. But God is only one. And all the different religions, whether Christian or not, stand for the effort the people of the world are making to understand Him rightly. Once we get that idea clearly we'll find that our religions draw us together instead of driving us apart. That's what they do now, they drive us apart; but the thing I wanted you to remember all your life is the force of that little syllable, l-i-g. It gives you the soul of the word, and therefore the soul of the thing. You might call religion the great universal ligament. It binds the universe in one—men to God, and God to men, and men to each other. And it's not a thing as to which we can pick and choose. It's an obligation. Do you know what an obligation is?"

"It's something you can't help doing, isn't it?"

"That's near enough. Now divide that word into syllables."

The boy began. "O-b, ob; l-i-g—— Why, there's the same thing again."

"Yes, there's the same thing again, and it's the last I'm going to point out. Religion is not only the great bond, but it's a bond you can't run away from. It binds you whether you want to be bound by it or not. Some people think— I've thought so myself—that you can give up religion. But you can't, not any more than you can give up the sky or the air or the light or the darkness. You're *obliged* to accept them. You might say I don't believe in day and night;

but would that keep the sun from rising and going down?"

"Why, no."

"Then to say you've given up religion is just as futile. You can't do it. No more can religion give up you. It's obliged to hold the mental universe together, and one day we shall see that better than we do to-day."

There was a sound in the front drawing room. Mabel came in, radiant with the outside air, with Ellie clinging to her skirt. The boy danced toward them.

"Oh, Mother, Father's been telling me all about religion."

"No," Leroy called after him, "not all about it. Only one little thing just as a beginning. It's like the cement floor of the cellar over which you build your house."

"But shan't we go on and build the house, Father?"

Leroy laughed. "That I can't promise you. I'm afraid that the utmost we can do will be to bring a few stones and put them on top of each other, in the hope of laying a foundation."

CHAPTER II

WHAT IS THE OLD TESTAMENT?

LEROY foresaw what Bobby's next question would be as soon as they received the list of articles he was to bring to the Doolittle School. Having been a Doolittle boy himself, he remembered now that this had been among his own requirements. Bobby was to have so many shirts, so many suits of underclothes, so many pairs of socks, and at the very end of the catalogue, as if a little ashamed of itself, there was the laconic mention of "1 Bible." As yet Bobby didn't really know what a Bible was, but nothing was so sure as that he would ask.

In anticipation of that day Leroy laid in a stock of Biblical literature and began to read. But he didn't read very far. His own thoughts he found more stimulating to himself than those of other people. Once other people had

supplied him with the ruling facts, marking
the lines along which he was to ruminate, he
was equal to the rumination.

His chief wish was to supply the boy with a
thread that would lead him through the Biblical labyrinth into which the Doolittle system of reading the Book had entangled him.
He understood that the same system was still
in operation. At morning prayers they read a
chapter of the Old Testament; at evening
prayers a chapter of the New. The chapters
were chosen so as to cover the outlines of both
Testaments in the course of the school year. But
the reading was reading only. The boys represented so many varieties of parents, and the
parents so many varieties of religion, that ex-
position was taboo.

From his own experience Leroy considered
this sort of reading worse than none at all.
Raising all the difficulties of the most difficult
book in the world, it allayed none of them. He
clearly remembered how he and the other boys,
being left without a clue to what with a little
explanation they could have understood, had

turned it into ridicule. He recalled too how gladly they would have accepted anything in the way of common-sense interpretation. Their ridicule was on the surface only; in the heart of their hearts they were reverent. They were eager, too, for some sort of steering through the mysteries of life. Of those mysteries they all talked more than their elders and teachers supposed they did, and pondered on them more than they talked. There was not one of them, he would have said, who beneath his levity and light-mindedness was not essentially serious. The years before them were so full of gigantic things to swing that any of them would have welcomed help in swinging them.

In a vague and general way they had heard that there was such help in the Bible. But the Bible as read to them, or as given to them to read, consisted largely of episodes they could not but call preposterous. At the opening of the school year they began with the story of Creation, going on to the details of Adam and Eve and the serpent. Over these they cracked the customary jokes. The habit of joking once begun ran throughout the school session. They joked about the Tower of Babel, about the plagues of Egypt, about Balaam and his ass. When there was nothing to joke about they considered the reading a failure. It was the worst possible preparation for the influence of religion in the life, and as such Leroy was anxious to forestall it in the case of his little boy.

So with the help of a few books on history, on criticism, on excavation, he read the Bible with a zeal he had never expected to bestow on it. Little by little he found himself reading not just for the sake of answering the boy's questions but from interest of his own. There was really a great deal in it, he kept saying to himself, once you got the hang of it. By the hang of it he meant a motive. A motive that would run through three thousand years of time, and be as imperative at the end of them as it had been at the beginning, must be one that would dominate civilization and ages. Such a motive would render the riddle of the Sphinx relatively trivial; and one day it flashed on him that he had found it.

That is, he had found the motive that satisfied himself. Doubtless there were others to satisfy other people. A work so vast in its measurements and so varied in its applications must have almost as many aspects as it would have readers of its pages; but the one which he had discovered would be the one for him. It would make no difference that hundreds of thousands had discovered it before him; neither would it make any difference that hundreds of thousands who knew the Book far more thoroughly than he had passed it by to discover something else. The fact remained that he had found the golden wire on which he could coherently string every incident and utterance between Genesis and Malachi, and see its chief significance.

He kept as yet to the Old Testament because it was the one which had given him most trouble. When he had thought of it at all it had been to say to himself that the modern world had outlived it, and that nowadays it did more harm than good. For a people who had conducted the Great War with so much

chivalry to enemies on all sides this record of
bloodshed, treachery, and vindictiveness was
too much of a shock. For years he had been
making a bogey of this shock, till catching now
a glimpse of a drama cosmic in its immensity.

He himself invited the boy's questions by
bringing home a Bible containing maps, com-
ments, and all sorts of data to make the reading
of it more comprehensible. Bobby accepted it
with the interest he gave to all his preparations
for boarding school, but for a day or two he
said nothing. Then one afternoon when they
were again alone together he brought up his
first question out of a spell of profound meditation.

"Father, what's the Bible for?"

Leroy lowered the paper which hid his face.
"Do you remember what I said about religion
a few days ago?"

"Yes, you said it was a bond, and the syllable
l-i-g stood for its real meaning. You said it was
the ligament that bound men to God, and God
to men, and men to each other."

"Well, then, the Bible is the history of how

we found that out. It isn't the history of religion. It's the history of men while they were discovering the purpose of religion."

"Is it true history?"

"It's true history to the extent that men of two thousand, and sometimes of three thousand, years ago understood the truth. Truth never changes, but our understanding of it does. Even in my lifetime, which hasn't been so very long, our understanding of truth has taken at least two tremendous leaps. When I was your age it wouldn't have been true to say that men could fly about in heavier-than-air machines; neither would it have been true to say that we could carry the music of an orchestra thousands of miles away without the use of wires. Had anybody said that we could the rest of us would have been obliged to deny it. By the time you yourself are fifty years of age things will have come true which now we should laugh at if anybody told us they were possible. Do you see? The world changes so quickly that an old-fashioned history is almost as much out of date as an old-fashioned novel."

"And is the Bible an old-fashioned history?"

"It might be, except for its absolute sincerity. Whatever it says is true to truth as truth was understood at the time of writing. It may not be true to what we understand as facts to-day, but it's true to what were understood as facts a great many centuries ago. Facts take a different look according as they're viewed by different ages. We can see that even among ourselves. Ellie at seven hasn't the same comprehension of facts that you have at twelve; and you at twelve haven't the same comprehension of facts as I have at thirty-six. Now the writers of the Bible, of whom there were a great many, were as wide apart in their development as Ellie and you and I. Some of them were at my stage; some of them at yours; some of them at Ellie's; and some go far, far back into the prehistoric. Do you know what the prehistoric is?"

Bobby shook his head. "I'm not sure that I do."

"Pre- means before. Sometimes you'll see an old building of which you're told that it's pre-Revolutionary. That means——"

"That it was built before the Revolution. Yes; I see."

"And the prehistoric came——"

"Before there was any history. But why wasn't there a history?"

"How could there be when no one knew how to write? You might say that the line between the historic and the prehistoric was drawn when the Egyptians invented their hiero-glyphs. You know what they are, don't you?"

The boy having said that he did know, Leroy went on to sketch the history of the alphabet, having for this purpose read up on it in an encyclopædia at the club.

"But an alphabet could be of no more than a limited use so long as it could only be cut into rocks or engraved on clay tablets. There could have been no free writing till the intro-duction of paper. Paper was first made from the inner bark of the Egyptian papyrus— *biblos* it was called—about two thousand years before Christ. As a matter of fact, the first meaning attached to the word which has since came to stand for the Holy Scriptures was

simply that fibre of the paper reed. Only in
the second place did it come to be applied to
books, which the Greeks called *biblia* because
of the material they were written on. Then in
the third it was given to the Holy Books as
representing the highest use to which writing
materials could be put. That's another little bit
of the history of words of which we were talking the last time, that our word 'Bible' still
keeps an echo of the name—*biblos*—given to
the fibre of the paper reed more than two thousand years ago."

Leroy went on to explain that as soon as men
secured a supply of pens, ink, and paper, they
set themselves to preserve that mass of prehistoric knowledge which had come to them
by word of mouth. Not only one person did it,
but a number. The prehistoric knowledge did
not belong to the Hebrews alone; it seems to
have been general. The Assyrians and Babylonians certainly possessed it in substance similar to that handed down among the Hebrews.
Such variations as there were could be at-
tributed to the differing mentalities of those

who repeated the tradition. On the lips of the Babylonians and Assyrians it tended to become gross; the Hebrew, with a higher ideal of God in his mind, refined this crudity away, transcribing the knowledge as a spiritual vehicle. A number of people worked at that, and if Bobby would bring him his Bible he would show him that there were three right at the beginning of the Book of Genesis.

Bobby having returned with his volume, Leroy pointed out to him the double account of Creation given in the first two chapters of Genesis, with a third account beginning with Chapter Five. This was evidence at once that the book was a compilation, not an original document. In the first chapter God was spoken of simply as God; in the second he had become Jehovah God. In the first story of the primitive human race they are grouped under the masculine and feminine, as Adam and Eve. In the second, beginning with Chapter Five, they are mentioned as Adam only: "Male and female created he them, and blessed them and called their name Adam."

From something said by one of his chums
at school a doubt as to the value of these chapters had lodged in Bobby's mind. "But it is all
true?"

"I should say," his father endeavoured to
explain to him, "that it was condensed truth.
The knowledge that had been accumulating
for perhaps six or eight thousand years, during
which time nothing could be written down,
would have to be condensed in order to allow
the mind to deal with it. To me the marvellous
thing is that this outline follows so closely that
which modern science has traced for us. You
must remember that science is purely a modern
thing, that the ancients knew nothing about it.
Still less did they know about it in the ages
called prehistoric. Even in the Middle Ages
such science as they understood was full of
errors, and mixed with superstition. It's not
much more than two hundred years since we've
tried to observe closely and note what we observed; and hardly a hundred since we've been
able to make practical use of what we'd been
acquiring."

Bobby brought his skepticism further into play. "But the world wasn't made in six days, was it?"

Leroy replied that it seemed to him that people had been making of those six days an unnecessary bugbear. If we had to go to the Bible for scientific knowledge it would be quite another thing. But we went to the Bible to find the laws of the spiritual life as the ages had discovered them. What did it matter if prehistoric man measured the stages through which Creation took place by days with a morning and evening or by eons of ages when he knew that God had evoked it? That was the one important thing, and of it he was sure. Modern readers, eager to reconcile prehistoric tradition with their up-to-date science, suggested that these days with mornings and evenings were in reality indefinite periods of time, but that seemed to him a mere quibbling with words. What it really amounted to was that the week of seven days, with the seventh day as one of rest, had been observed from immemorial time, and this connection of each day with a

cycle of creative development was meant as a
kind of consecration. When you came to think
of it, it was a noble idea, rich in poetry. Why try
to read in terms of hard modern fact that which
should only be seen in its light of magnificent
beauty? When it came to magnificent beauty
if Bobby would only listen while he read the
opening words of the Bible he would see for
himself how sonorous language could become
when infused with a majestic thought.

Leroy read slowly and impressively:

"In the beginning God created the heaven
and earth. And the earth was without form,
and void; and darkness was upon the face of
the deep. And the Spirit of God moved upon
the face of the waters. And God said, Let there
be Light; and there was Light. And God saw
the Light that it was good."

Bobby's eyes glistened. "Fine, isn't it? But
it's the way you read it, Father."

"It reads itself. It can't be read in any other
way. And what I want you to remember is that
this is not science; it's beauty. I've read somewhere within a day or two that what's told us

here in the Book of Genesis bears the same relation to modern knowledge as a picture by Turner does to an ordinance map. An ordinance map is excellent in its way, but why demand that a picture by Turner shall be just like it? The two serve different purposes. When these things puzzle you, or when you hear other fellows turning them into ridicule, try to remember that. We go to the Bible not to learn whether the world was made in six days or in cycles of ten thousand years apiece. We go to learn that it was made by God. God is bound to it; it is bound to God; and the expression of that band is—what now?"

"It's religion, isn't it?"

"Yes, it's religion; not this religion or that religion, but religion in general. That means to me the one great fact which the Old Testament tries to work out."

Bobby showed that his knowledge of the Bible went further than his father had supposed. "But there never was an Adam and Eve and a serpent that talked to them, now was there?"

"That's more of what I've called condensed knowledge. In it thousands of years of progress are compressed into a few incidents. When you see that, it will become not a source of jokes for the funny man but one of the most stupendous things ever done by man. I don't believe that we shall ever know much about the Old Testament till we try to rescue these opening pages from the cheap smart-Aleck, and reverence what they mean. If we don't catch the first note it isn't of much use to go on."

It was a pity, Leroy explained, that the terms "Adam" and "Eve" had been taken by our translators to be proper names. In reality they were not names at all. Adam was simply Man; Eve was Life or Woman or Mother according to the shade of significance you attached to the word. The prehistoric bards who to keep this ancient knowledge from being lost first told the tale around the primitive campfires used the method we now know as personification in order to get conciseness. Knowing already what conciseness was Bobby was asked for ex-

amples of personification and produced John
Bull and Uncle Sam. These suited his father
exactly.

"You see Uncle Sam is not one American,
he's every American; and John Bull is not one
Englishman, but all Englishmen taken together. In the same way Adam was not an individual man; he was Mankind in general,
while the chronicle expressly says that Man
called his wife's name Life or Mother because
she was the source of life to everyone born.

"So what we meet in the opening pages of
the Old Testament," he continued, "is not a
pair of individuals, but *the human race*. Moreover, it's the human race at a certain stage of
its development. Its elementary epochs are behind it. It has reached the age of reason. It is
primitive reason as yet, but none the less a
long step in advance. Three great concepts it
has already worked out: a consciousness of
God, the perception that in human conduct
there is both good and evil, the suggestion of a
future life. Because Man has hitherto been un-

equal to responsibility he has been innocent.
Now he takes the next great step in his development in being subjected to the test.

"The Bible," he continued further, "intro-
duces us to the human race just at the point
where it begins its great spiritual struggle.
Evil suggestion, too, is personified; and nothing
more expressive of subtle insinuation than a
serpent could have been selected. The Tree of
the Knowledge of Good and Evil becomes, according to this sinister suggestion, the Tree to
Be Desired to Make One Wise. That too was
exactly to the point. You can see for yourself
that temptation often comes in the guise of
adding to one's experience."

Now if Bobby were to take his Bible and
read this story as the starting point of the long
spiritual fight on which the human race is still
engaged it would make everything else in the
Old Testament fall relatively into place. There
would be a great deal that he wouldn't understand but of which he would always be able to
say that it was a detail in that struggle upward.
The human race would be shown as doing a

great many evil things as well as some good ones, but the general effect would be forward. It was made to advance, and with all its progress God was closely connected. Even if He was a primitive God, who worked when He was active, and rested when He was tired, and walked and talked with men in quite a human way, there were already in Him elements of mercy as well as of justice, and of pity and grace for the human race when it had sinned. That is, He was already in their conception of Him a loving God. He was loving in little things as well as in great ones. As Man and Woman began their age-long struggle toward Him he not only promised them ultimate spiritual victory, but in their immediate helplessness He showed them the benefits to be found in work and clad them in coats of skin. He corrected them, but He never deserted them. This complete association of God with the interests of the human race, collectively and individually, was to Leroy's way of thinking the one main fact which the Old Testament set forth.

"We see that further," he went on to Bobby, "in the story of the conflict between the pastoral and agricultural activities of mankind which is given in the Bible under the personified names of Cain and Abel. This is not a tale of the murder of one man by another. To consider it that is to dwarf it, and deprive it of its significance. It initiates the contest between two great classes for the domination of their time. Cain was a tiller of the ground, Abel a keeper of sheep. We know that the first step taken toward the condition we call civilized was in keeping cattle. To a migratory people, who did not as yet know the use of metals, cattle supplied everything they needed, milk, meat, skins, bones, and horn. Neither did they know as yet the uses of fruit and grain. When fruit and grain were introduced the pastoral classes resented it, just as in the Middle Ages the populace resented the building of houses with windows and chimneys, or as the peasant worker resented the construction of railways and the use of machinery in the early part of the Nineteenth Century. As usual God was claimed by the ultra-conservative. 'He had respect unto Abel and his offering, but unto Cain and his offering he had not respect.' It is always so. In the march of progress the Church is generally the last to move. Those who undertake to speak for God nearly always represent Him as being on the side of the older ways. As life became more settled, and the new industry of the farmer killed the earlier one of the herdsman, God was invoked to dispossess the agriculturalist. This He is shown as doing by checking the tendency to a settled life, and sending Cain, its representative, into the land of Nod, which means a life of wandering. Wandering and agriculture being incompatible, the herdsman class was supposed to be avenged."

That these are personifications is evident from the fact that the traditions take for granted the existence of a partly populated world. Leroy made it clear to Bobby that there was no question here of a First Man and a First Woman with two sons, two brothers, as the only occupants of the planet. Anyone who met Cain could slay him. In other words, Cain went forth as a fugitive among strangers. The existence of strangers is assumed. The assumption is further borne out when Man and Woman bring forth another son, who typifies another tendency. Cain and Abel represent material interests, with the inception of that industrial warfare which is still a prime element in social life. But there was a third blend in the human consciousness, the intellectual and spiritual. Seth, otherwise The Appointed One, represented that. Seth was the beginning of the spiritual development. His son was Enos, another word for Man, and practically the equivalent of Adam. That is to say, a new type of man came to birth in the world, one which cared more for the spiritual than for the material. This man having come, "then," the Bible goes on, "men began to call on the name of the Lord." God having so closely associated Himself with Man, Man began at last to associate himself with God. But it is always Enos, Man, Mankind, not Enos as the name of an individual.

Most of these names, Leroy had read, were

difficult of interpretation because they probably belonged to languages altogether lost. Here and there was one that could be traced to a Hebrew or a Babylonian source, and so made to yield up its significance. But many of them occur in mere snatches thrown in among more coherent traditions so as not to be wholly forgotten. In the main, however, each of them stood for a moment in the story of human advance.

For example, in Cain the settled life persisted to such a degree that men began to live in cities. In Jabal, a name connected with Abel, the pastoral life persisted, too, but with an element of progress even here, since the herdsman who in earlier stages had presumably dwelt beneath the open sky began to live in tents. In Jubal, "the father of such as handle the harp and the organ," we have the origin of the arts. In Tubal, the smith, we see Man coming out at last from the Stone Age, and acquiring the mastery of metals. With the emergence from the Stone Age, and the advance of Man into the practice of the arts and crafts, civilization in the modern sense may be said to have begun.

Leroy explained to Bobby that he had lingered over these opening pages of the Bible because they seemed to him in many ways the most important. "They strike the keynote. They lay down the theme on which all the rest of the Old Testament is but an elaboration. That theme might be said to be Man's long, slow fight to conquer himself, to conquer the world of nature, to attain to God. These fragments of the prehistoric show us how he began. They show us, too, that he must have had the seed of great things in himself to have begun at all. If you had to find a title that would cover the whole of the Old Testament, putting its meaning into two or three words, you might call it *The Way Up*. It is not a way that Man follows without many a slip backward, or without many a spell of turning altogether aside from it. But with all kinds of sins and sorrows and desertions and perversions the struggle is forever taken up again toward a great Further On.

We've come a long way already, and we've a longer still to go, but we'll get there in the end."

When Leroy had ceased speaking Bobby remained for some time absorbed in his own meditations. "But why," he asked, then, "didn't God make us so that we'd be there already, without the trouble of fighting our own way?"

"And take from us the biggest fun of existence! It isn't having things, you know, that gives the zest to life. It's working hard to get them."

CHAPTER III

WHAT IS THE NEW TESTAMENT?

BOBBY was a thoughtful boy but not what could be called a pious one. You might quite correctly have said that his interest in the Bible did not spring from piety at all, but from a desire to know things. Even so it was chiefly a desire to know what his father knew. To know what his father didn't know stirred his zeal but slightly.

For some days after their last discussion he did not bring up the subject again. Leroy had by this time adopted a policy of letting him be the first to speak. That he was turning over in his mind what had been said the other day the father could tell by the way he kept the Bible within reach, studied the maps, read the historical and other data, though without a comment. Still without a comment he read one

day four or five of the earlier chapters of
Genesis, seeming to reflect on them afterward.
Like his father he had the cogitating mind,
the mind which having received a certain
amount of outside stimulation does the rest
for itself. Leroy was glad of this, because it
often filled their silences with something more
profitable to the lad than continuous explanations.

In fact, he seemed to satisfy himself with
thinking before asking a question at all. When
he did so it came forth spontaneously.

"Father, isn't there another part of the Bible
besides the Old Testament?"

Turning a page of his newspaper, Leroy
glanced at the headlines while answering.
"Yes, there's the New Testament."

"What's the difference between them?"

Having expected this question, Leroy had
framed an answer in advance. "We said of the
Old Testament that it was the story of the
struggle of men to reach God. Well, I suppose
we might call the New Testament that of the
only Man who ever truly reached Him."

"That was Jesus, wasn't it?"

Leroy confessed that it was.

"But Jesus was the same as God, anyhow, wasn't He?"

Leroy reflected. "Do you know," he said, at last, "that's something I'd rather not talk to you about? It isn't that I don't believe it, but I can't explain it. I can't explain it because I don't understand it; and what I don't understand I'd rather not discuss."

"Other people," Bobby objected, "who don't understand it discuss it. Aunt Susie does. It was she who told me. She said that Jesus was the same as God, and when I asked her how she said she didn't know, but that I was to believe it just the same, because He was."

"Yes, and I think that sort of talk is a mistake. Where there's so much that we do understand I think we ought to keep to it. I suppose Aunt Susie told you of the Father, the Son, and the Holy Ghost, the Trinity——"

"Yes, that's what she called it."

"But she didn't say that in speaking of the Father and the Son we're using words in a sense quite different from that which they commonly bear, did she?"

"I don't think she did. Then what sense do we use them in?"

"In a high and mystical sense which we ordinary people hardly ever seize. But the trouble is we talk as if we did. Every now and then we begin on the subject of what is known as the Virgin Birth. You might suppose to hear us then that God the Father and the Virgin Mary had a child together, much as your Uncle Tom and your Aunt Susie had a child together. In the same way that your little cousin is half English and half American, because your Aunt Susie is an Englishwoman and your Uncle Tom a New Yorker, so this other Child was half human, half divine, through a kind of physical inheritance. But that couldn't be the meaning of the Virgin Birth. Jesus could not have been the Son of God in the same sense that you're my son, or that I'm the son of my father."

"Well, then," Bobby demanded, with some

indignation, "how did He get into the Trinity?"

"That's what I don't know, and so I can't tell you. I've tried to read up about it, but even so I don't understand. But one thing I can tell you, and it would be well if you did your best never to forget it, and it's this, that when we speak of Three Persons in One God we can't mean Persons in the sense that you're a person, and your mother's a person, and I'm a person. It often happens that when great new truths have to be expressed words must be wrenched from their old significance and put to new uses. Something like that has occurred here. The Persons in the Godhead may mean aspects of the Godhead or functions in the Godhead, or any of several possibilities. But you see from the very words I have to choose how little is to be gained by our discussing it. We should only get farther and farther out of our depth, shouldn't we?"

Bobby having admitted that he thought this probable, Leroy went on to another point in the same connection. "At the same time, old boy, I'm glad you've brought the subject up, because it gives me a chance to put you on your guard against the very common feeling that if in religion there's something you don't understand you can therefore dismiss it as not true. We don't feel that about anything else—only about religion. Now I should like you to be clear that we ought to give religion the same chance that we give to other subjects. That is something that very few people do. And yet there are a great many things in the world which you and I don't understand, but which we should never hesitate to take on trust because we know that competent people do understand them. For example, I don't understand the laws of wireless. I've had them explained to me time and time again, and yet even now wireless seems to me miraculous. I don't understand how astronomers can measure the size, let us say, of that great star, Betelgeuse, and tell us the number of light years it is away from us, but I should never think of denying that they can. And yet when I was twenty years of age I refused to believe in the Trinity be-

cause I didn't understand it, and for the same
reason almost gave up my whole belief in
God."

Never having heard so much of his father's
spiritual history, the boy's eyes were eager with
interest.

"And I should like to feel," Leroy went on,
"that I had put you on your guard against the
same mistake. There are many things about
religion that are perfectly simple, just as there
are about science, art, mathematics, or any
other study. But to reject the simple because
you see that there are difficult things, too, is
like rejecting the rules of addition and sub-
traction because you have not yet mastered the
principles of algebra. Do you get anything of
what I mean?"

Bobby considered this question before answering. "I see," he said, thoughtfully, at last,
"that it's better not to worry about what we
can't understand when there's so much that
we can."

"That's exactly it," Leroy replied, proud of
his son's clear-headedness; "and if we can

leave the more difficult themes to one side then, I think, we're free to approach the most beautiful subject in the world."

"Would that be Jesus, too?"

"Yes, that would be Jesus, too. I call Him the most beautiful subject in the world because, as I've been reading about Him lately, I find Him so full of charm. That's the point of view from which I should like to talk of Him, because it's new to me. I think He gives us our highest ideal of a gentleman. He is everybody's equal. He never condescends to humble; He is never ill at ease among the great. It is not so much that He meets people on their own level, or that He raises them to His. There is no question of a level of any kind, nothing but a broad, sympathetic human basis on which everyone has the opportunity of being his very best. Even between those whom we divide into good people and bad people He seems to make no distinction. His manner is perfect to them all. While it would not be fair to say that He is more deferential to women than to men, yet in the brief glimpses we have of Him with women

He is the embodiment of a simple natural courtesy that has nothing to do with sex. He might be said to be the first example of what was afterward known as chivalry. With the Woman of Samaria, whose reputation was an evil one, His bearing is exactly what it is to Mary and Martha, who were ladies of position in their small community. As an example of good breeding I don't think we've ever had anyone to equal Him."

With eyes of burning interest Bobby waited for his father to go on.

"It was the more remarkable because it was something new in human nature. There had been plenty of instances of men who were both kind and courteous, but never one before who was kind and courteous universally. Every other kind man made exceptions in his kindliness; every other courteous man was courteous in a narrow circle only. He was not supposed to be courteous to the poor, or to servants, or to people of bad character. This Man brought with Him a code of manners in which the fact that you were a human being gave you a claim to the best that He could offer you. As I come back to the study of His character after a good many years of thinking little about Him this lovableness that I call charm is the first thing that impresses me."

"And what's the next?"

Leroy took his time before replying. "His goodness," he said then. "In some respects that goodness is the most amazing human thing that's ever been in the world. Perhaps a sidelight on it will give you a more vivid conception of it than anything else I could say. I noticed it in reading the New Testament a little while ago. It was this. He was asking His disciples what the people said about Him. They told Him that some said He was John the Baptist come back to life; that to others He was Elijah or some other ancient prophet risen again. 'But whom do ye say that I am?' was the question He asked next. And Peter told Him. 'Thou art the Christ, the Son of the Living God.' Now when you come to think of it that was perhaps the most remarkable testimony to His goodness anyone had ever received. You must remember that these men had been living in the closest intimacy with Him for something like two years. They had heard everything He had said, seen everything He had done. They knew that He lived as they did, dressed as they did, spoke as they did, had the same human needs that they had themselves. And yet they could say that to Him—that He was the Christ, the Son of the Living God. It's all very well for us to say it, at this distance of time, and with all we've heard about His death on the Cross, His resurrection from the dead, and His ascension into heaven; but none of these things had happened at that time, and all they saw was a man outwardly like themselves, as we see when we look around us. And yet they could say that astounding thing to Him, that they believed Him to be the Son of the Living God. To them at least He had proved Himself to be the son of God by making Himself as good as God."

"Did He make Himself as good as God? I thought He was born like that, and couldn't help it."

"I know that that's a common impression, but it seems to me to take away most of the honour due to him. Without pretending to know all about it I can't help believing that at first, at any rate, it was as hard for Him to be what we call good as it is for anybody else. We know He could feel temptation. Not only are we expressly told that He faced every temptation we have to meet, but others that we are spared. There were what we call His three great temptations in the wilderness which could only have come to a soul much bigger than any ordinary man, and must have been fierce in proportion."

Since Bobby had not heard of them Leroy summarized briefly the gospel account. As he began it Mabel slipped into the room unnoticed by her son, signalling to her husband to continue while she took a seat out of sight. Though shy of giving his explanations in presence of a skeptical spirit like his wife, he took his courage in both hands and went on.

Jesus had been a boy, and had doubtless met and mastered all the testing any boy is subjected to. He had been a young man, and from hints in the New Testament He had been spared nothing of what a young man has to face. But victory on this lower ground had been relatively easy. The real trial came when in solitude with God He had finished all His preparations for His public work of the redemption of the world.

Then, according to the gospels, "He was led by the Spirit into the wilderness to be tempted of the devil." This mention of the devil could be understood in a number of ways, the simplest of which was that personification of great forces to which from their earliest history the Hebrews had been prone. Over the question as to whether or not our Lord and His apostles believed in a personal devil a great deal of ink had been spilled, when in reality it was an unimportant one. Leroy thought it probable that on subjects of this kind their knowledge was not beyond that of their fellow countrymen, or if it was that they adopted the common phraseology. The essential thing to know was that certain ideas were suggested to the mind of

Christ, and that He considered them long enough to see that attractive as they might be at first their general effect would be wrong.

The first was that having worked it out to His satisfaction that He was the Son of God He could command the stones about Him in the wilderness to be made bread. Undoubtedly He could. There are indications that the un-chronicled years between boyhood and thirty were filled with the demonstrations of His power over matter. The beginning of what are commonly known as His miracles, that of the turning of the water into wine at the marriage feast in Cana, was probably a repetition of what He had done more than once at home. Whatever were the meanings He gave to the expression "Son of God" that which St. Paul calls "the Son of God with power" was in all probability one of them. The suggestion here was not the relatively mean one that He could turn the stones into bread to satisfy His hunger after His long fast—that would have been too petty for so great a soul!—it was one of the approach to His work. By the mere speaking

of a word He had at His command a means of
triumphant beneficence. In that bitter hungry
world there need be no more hunger, no more
privation. In the Kingdom of Heaven there
would be bread enough and to spare. It would
be a wonderful beginning to the gospel of
peace and good will toward men; and for what
other reason had He perfected His lordship
over the creative secrets of Nature? It was not
a scientific lordship; it went farther back than
that, back to the timeless ages when "In the
beginning was the Word, and the Word was
with God, and the Word was God. All things
were made by Him, and without Him was not
anything made that was made."

Then, too, there was the ease with which the
world would believe in a Saviour who came
with universal benefactions, as contrasted with
one who appeared with comparatively empty
hands. He would be the proof of His own assertions. When He taught them of a God liberal and loving He need look no farther than
His own achievements. For Him as for them it
would be only the demonstration of abundance

rather than that of Calvary and the Cross. The prospect must have been a very fair one.

The same strain ran through both the other appeals to His greatheartedness. A Saviour who descended into one of the temple courts surrounded and protected by twelve legions of angels would at once have been the darling of those He came to save. If the innumerable poor of the world were to profit when the stones were made into bread, the spiritual Israel would welcome the Son of God who came with the Father's grace so visibly upon Him. Not what He would be spared could have been uppermost in this man's thoughts, but the sign from heaven openly attesting to the fact that He was the Word which had been from the beginning. No denials, no rejections, no such error as that of coming to His own while His own received Him not would be possible to such a people before such a Son of God. There would have been nothing mysterious, baffling, or paradoxical, nothing of the King on the Cross, in this spiritual hero. He would come angelically guarded to His own; His own would receive Him; and to as many as received Him He would give the power to become the sons of God in themselves.

On an even larger scale was the use of the kingdoms of the world and the glory of them to reconcile man to His Father. That was what it would come to. This Saviour-Cæsar would soon have the world at His feet. If Xerxes, Alexander, and Julius could do it in their way He could in His, climbing from honour to honour, and annexing new countries to the glory of His power through no other agency than love. It could be done. He could make Himself the Imperial Redeemer, none the less a redeemer for His crown and throne. God reigning on earth had been as much a vision in the heart of mankind as the Man of Sorrows, despised, rejected, and acquainted with grief. In His approach to His work which should He make His ideal? It was a choice between the quick and facile conversion of the world to a religion brilliant with court and ceremonial and the long, slow, toilsome struggle which had been man's from the beginning of time.

"But, Father, could the devil have given Him all the kingdoms of the world and the glory of them?"

"I don't see that that matters so long as we know He could have taken them. The kingdoms of this world and the glory of them have generally been at the disposal of those who were able to seize them. A number of men have done so: Alexander of Macedon, Cæsar, Charlemagne, Napoleon, among others. This man was stronger than them all, and we can depend upon it that if for His own purposes He needed the kingdoms of the world and the glory of them He could have had them. I don't know how, of course. I speak only on the general principles of strength. He had worked out a system of power which in comparison would have made Cæsar and Napoleon weaklings. I suppose no greater renunciation could ever have been made than His refusal of what seemed like this tremendous aid to doing good and helping on the progress of mankind. The easing of the human lot was part of His mission that He had most at heart. But just where

His means could have served most effectively
He had to let them go."

"But why did He? Why shouldn't He have
taken the kingdoms of the world and glory of
them, and done a lot of good with them?"

Probably, Leroy pointed out, because He
foresaw that the kingdoms of this world would
not increase in spiritual power, while the Kingdom of God would lose it. Bobby must see by
his experience in school how little there was
of great value that could be picked up cheaply
and quickly. Even a boy of twelve must understand that such attractions as the kingdoms of
the world and their glory might possess for
man would in the end prove corrosive and de-
structive. Once this was realized the Saviour
of the world had no choice but to turn His back
on all such dangerous aids.

And in doing so He left Himself no choice
but the way of suffering. Here again it was not
suffering in itself that He shrank from. That is
something we all have to face, many with an
anguish equal to dying on the Cross and even
exceeding it. The peculiarity of His case was

to be rejected, persecuted, hounded to death by those for whom His heart was brimming over in love and to whom His mission of salvation was to be tendered first of all.

"But," Bobby interposed, "if He was so good why didn't everybody like Him?"

"That is one of the greatest mysteries of human nature. Instinctively we dislike the good. If we hear anyone spoken of as good we have a prejudice against him in advance. Where for any reason it puts us to shame we turn against it actively. When Jesus appeared among men His very presence was a challenge to the whole manner of life around Him. He came as a champion of the unhappy, the persecuted, the downtrodden, the poor, the sick, the masses who were considered to own no rights. It was a world in which in every country, Jew and Gentile, rights had been gathered into the hands of a few, while the vast hordes of the people had been dispossessed. He came as the Great Restorer, not through methods of violence, but through the action of love. When John the Baptist sent to Him to ask the question, 'Art thou He that should come, or do we look for another?' His answer was, 'Go and tell John *again*'—there was, I am sure, some emphasis on that *again*—'the things which ye do hear and see. The blind receive their sight, the lame walk, the deaf hear, the lepers are cleansed, the dead are raised up, and the poor have the gospel preached unto them, and blessed is he whosoever shall not be offended in me.' This last sentence gives the key to what He dreaded most, hatred directed against Himself. And yet from a world hardened in indifference to suffering, with no sense of pity, these acts of mercy were revolutionary. They were crimes against the common good. They made man as man an object of compassion and even of honour."

Leroy went on to indicate another cause for enmity toward Him. In among a people whose religion consisted of dead formalities, ritual observances, conventional ceremonies, an elaborate outward round with no corresponding motive in the inner life. He came as the exponent of that true, simple, primal religion whose test is in action and whose inspiration is the love of God. Its appeal was tremendous and almost instantaneous. Thousands followed Him from place to place. To their religion of forms He became a menace. There were times when it looked as if He meant to destroy the Law and the Prophets. It was the most natural impulse in the world that the great conservative native rank and file should seek to do away with Him.

"But the point I am trying to make," Leroy explained further to Bobby, "is that when He renounced the aid of all the secret powers He had learned how to command He did so knowing that this rejection lay before Him. The purer He kept Himself from sin, the more bitterly sin would work its vengeance upon Him. Very well, then; let it come. He would meet it, bow before it, submit to the wringing from Him of the last drop of suffering, and then rise triumphant. I said He was the Son of God because He made Himself as good as God. For even God, had He put Himself into the hands of men for us to buffet as we chose, could have displayed no higher or more perfect heroism than this Man shows at every turn of His career. For this reason I want you to remember this when you hear half-fledged debaters talking of a Virgin Birth, a Trinity, a divinity of Christ, which they don't understand and would keep you from understanding—I want you to remember that here is a single great fact which hardly anyone would dispute and which you can always fall back upon: He made Himself as good as God, and therefore in some sense the equal of God. He did it in the face of great opposition, with a world against Him, but He did it so thoroughly that when it comes to comparing Him with God it is difficult for you and me not to see them as One."

A few silent minutes went by before Leroy began again. "You will not suppose for an instant that I'm saying all there is to be said on this great subject. I'm telling you only how I myself approach it. Besides which, this is only the beginning of many talks we shall have along these lines. It isn't all to end this evening, seeing that the subject itself is endless. Only that there's this that I should like to ask of you. When you want to talk of it to anyone talk to me first. Above all, don't get drawn into arguments on religion with fellows of your own age. If you're in a room where such arguments are going on don't take part in them, or take as little as possible. Remember how little we understand. None of us really has a right to an opinion on the subject unless it's a very reverent and humble one. Will you try to remember that?"

"Yes, Father, I will."

"Now, I think, you'd better be off to your supper."

As he passed through the front drawing room on his way out Bobby surprised his mother sitting in the shadow. "Hello, Mother! You there?" He kissed her and passed on.

Mabel herself came into the room where her husband was, and sat down. "It's very interesting, Chris, but how much do you think he'll remember of it all?"

"Possibly very little. But what I think he will never forget is that he and I have had these talks together. That will remain as something sweet and pleasant in his memory when perhaps much that I've been saying would have gone."

CHAPTER IV

WHAT IS A CHURCH?

IT WAS not till the end of his first holiday home
from Doolittle's that Bobby mentioned
churches. Though he referred to them from
time to time it was only incidentally and in
connection with other fellows. Religious instruction as given in the school was purely non-
sectarian. For pupils whose parents deemed
this insufficient there was the privilege of at-
tending, under the supervision of a master,
any one of half a dozen churches in the neighbouring town. "So-and-So goes to the Presby-
terian Church," Bobby would throw in, when
the occasion fitted; "so-and-so to the Episcopal." Then one day, after some such remark
as the foregoing, came the question Leroy had
been expecting for a week or more.

"Father, what's a church for? Why do we
have so many of them?"

75

"A church," Leroy began, with the definition he had prepared long ago, when Mabel interrupted him.

It was one of the afternoons when she was at home. They were not infrequent, since she was a good mother and took in her children's education the interest which sees that they go to the schools where they shall meet the children of the best families and get the same kind of teaching. This was from no cheap spirit of future social advantage of which she was not in need, but from the mental habit which takes the best for granted.

Religion never having been a subject which greatly occupied the old sporting family of Boltwing, Mabel had grown up with scarcely a trace of it in her thought. This does not mean that she never conformed to what other people did, but it was conforming only. It had no meaning for her, and when the children came along with their questions she was sorry to betray the fact of her ignorance. For the few weeks before Bobby went to Doolittle's she had been rather jealous of the almost intentional

way in which Leroy and he had kept their con-
ferences to themselves.

"Can't you wait a minute," she said now,
"while I take Ellie to her governess and tell
them what to do? I wish you'd take me in on
your wise discussions when I'm in the house. I
need instruction as much as even Ellie does."

Leroy and Bobby said what they could to
welcome her, while fearing she would be a
non-sympathetic member of their council.
Nevertheless, it was but a minute or two before she returned, bringing a bag of sewing
and settling herself in a corner. "Now I'm
ready," she sighed, as if an entertainment had
been prepared for her, and she was giving the
signal to begin. It was difficult to announce
such a subject to one, even a mother, who had
not shared in all the motives and half-motives
that had led up to it, so that Leroy could only
state bluntly that Bobby had just asked him
what a church was, and why we had so many
of them, and he was about to tell him what he
had thought out as an explanation.

"And I should so much like to hear," came

from Mabel, sympathetically enough. "Some of the things I overheard in your last talk with Bobby have stayed with me ever since. That very question, What is a church, and why do we have so many of them? has puzzled me more times than I can tell you."

"In the first place," Leroy replied, "we have not so many of them. I'm not speaking of the number of edifices, but in the way of religious bodies. People talk of our three hundred odd Christian sects as if each one had a church and congregation on every city block, but as a matter of fact the great majority of them are freak sects and hardly ever heard of. When it comes to those which concern ourselves we don't get much beyond half a dozen. In the great big vital thing called Christianity eight or ten points of view are by no means too many for it to need in presenting itself to the world. If there had never been but one school of the religion of Christ it would have meant that mankind had never taken it to its heart. Human nature has so many outlooks that where we make use of only one it means that we are relatively indifferent. The more interesting a subject is the more it will meet with difference of opinion. Admitting that the vastly greater number of our divisions exist in names only—often names which none of us have ever heard—that much-harried institution we call Christianity still has some ground for calling itself more or less of a unity."

Mabel stitched. "That's interesting, Chris; but what would the grounds be?"

"Chiefly the ways in which the churches have come into being. Each of them seems to have risen to meet the needs of large numbers of people who have come to think in a certain way. Each has been organized in such a manner as best to put that way of thinking into operation. If I had to make a definition of a church it would be something like this: A church is an organization for the development of Christian ideals from a certain point of view."

Mabel asked, drily, "What about the first church of all? Doesn't it come in for special rights and favours?"

"Possibly; if you could tell what it was. But

except for vestiges that early Church is gone apparently beyond recovery. The Founder of the Christian Religion seems to have left but a loosely organized group to carry on His work. His was not first of all an organization; it was first of all a teaching. We talk a great deal of Christ and His Church, as if He had foreseen hierarchies enlisted in His service, and sanctuaries like St. Peter's, the Kremlin, and St. Paul's dedicated to His honour; but so far is this from the case that I cannot see that what we moderns call a church was in His mind at all. Something *was* in His mind, something much greater than a church, and which will perhaps prove an ideal for the Church one day to fall back upon——"

"What was that, Father?"

"We shall see in a minute. All I want to make clear just now is that He seems to have had nothing in His mind in the way of a corporation. If it was a corporation it was so purely spiritual that even the apostles didn't wholly grasp its significance. Outwardly He was a Jew, and as a Jew Judaism was enough for Him. Within its limits He found—and seems to have expected to find—that extension of Judaism which others have developed since His time into the Christian Church. He Himself, as recorded in the gospels, says nothing about a Christian church. He mentions the word "church" only twice, and in neither case could it have been in any such sense as we use the word to-day. And what strikes me as strange is that as late as the date at which the gospels were written, which may have been any time between fifty and eighty years after His departure, the idea of a church was so little to the fore that the name occurs but on these two occasions. If it had been an institution He had in His mind and greatly cared about He would probably have talked of it at all times. If it had been any of the religious bodies which now claim to represent Him with so much authority the gospels ought to have rung with the fact that we were to expect and obey it. Where obedience is of such vast importance as some of the churches make out it seems to me— though of course I may be wrong—a most careless method to leave us without an inkling of the fact."

Though this was over Bobby's head it was not over Mabel's. "But if Christ didn't found the churches—or some of them—or one of them at least—who did?"

"They were evolved. They grew as they were required. They grew from the simplest beginnings, and apparently without foreseeing the direction they were taking. The name itself as used in the latter part of the New Testament is the vaguest possible—an assembly, a gathering, a congregation. We must always be careful not to read backward into the Scriptures the great regal meaning which the word has taken on since that time, but of which no one had any premonition then. What has become of the proudest syllables ever formed by human lips began as expressing the humblest kind of human need, that of getting together. When the Jews of this new way of thinking—who still did not expect to be driven out of Judaism—had need of coming together they called their reunions by the simplest name possible;

they were 'meetings.' They said the word as
unconsciously as old-fashioned English dis-
senters speak of 'going to meeting,' where we
say 'going to church.' In the same way the New
England colonists called their places of wor-
ship 'meeting houses,' a quaint name which it
seems a pity to have given up. Now, the name
'church'—*ecclesia*—meant simply 'a meeting,'
and if you can imagine the combined New
England meeting houses swelling into a vast
imperial body with claims to rule the world
through its conscience you would have some
idea of what actually took place."

Bobby knew enough history to follow this,
and ask: "Yes, but what made them swell?"

Leroy smiled. "A great many answers might
be given to that question, all with more or less
truth in them. My own feeling is that the
Church couldn't help itself. In general, I think,
we find that human life takes the line of least
resistance. Events arrange themselves like
mountains, leaving certain passes that you can
get through. But you must go through them,
or be blocked. So the Church had its way cut

out for it, and couldn't take any other. She was
obliged to become strong, or go under. In becoming strong she was compelled to use, without too many scruples, whatever weapons came
her way. Had she not done so the semi-barbaric
kings and emperors among whom she strove
would have pulled her down and made away
with her inheritance. As it was, they did it
whenever they got the opportunity. Luckily
for her, she had certain resources far more ter-
rifying to semi-civilized peoples than force of
arms could be against herself. She had hell fire.
Freely and easily she could commit to it all
who disobeyed her, while her victims scarcely
dared to question her sway over them. For
great rebels she had the dread arm of excom-
munication, in which the person thrust beyond
the means of grace was also thrust beyond all
human intercourse, those who served him,
spoke with him, or gave him so much as a cup
of cold water being placed under the same ban
as himself. As punishment for further defiance
there was the interdict, which could be laid on
the whole land, as it was for six years in Eng-

land in King John's time. During the interdict
there could be no exercise of the priestly office
for any purpose but the baptizing of infants,
so that those of the poor little innocents who
died, as so many of them did, should not go
to hell. Otherwise no service was held in any
church, no sermon was preached in any pulpit,
no sacrament was administered, no marriage
was performed, there were no rites for the sick
and dying, and no prayers at the burial of the
dead. A Church which could hold this menace
over peoples by whom these ministrations were
considered essential to their escape from eternal torment was in a strong position indeed. But
had it not been strong it might easily have been
swept away, and civilization in Europe, to say
nothing of the more spiritual side of life, been
left without a defender."

Bobby was deeply interested. "Could they
lay an interdict on the United States?"

His father smiled. "I think the time for such
severe measures must have gone by. We're not
much afraid of interdicts at present, nor of ex-
communication. The Church that once had all

that power has comparatively little nowadays
—notice that I'm not saying 'very little' but
'comparatively little'—and where once every
sovereign in Europe bowed before its throne
there are now only a few to do that homage."

"You must make some allowance," Mabel
put in, "for the fact that there are not so many
sovereigns in Europe, mustn't you?"

"Oh, but I think there are. It's a queer
American error that Europe is dishing its
kings and queens, because every now and then
one of them goes under. At present they have
some twelve or fourteen, all in active business,
and I doubt if there were so many even
in the Middle Ages. But one odd thing is
this, that the King of Great Britain, for example, although he is of the Anglican faith,
when he visits the Head of the Church, is
received with as much deference as if he were
still the faithful son that his far-away ances-
tors used to be. The same is true of every other
ruler. Tourists of all nationalities are admitted to his presence and get the same bless-
ing, so far as I could see when I went, as the

true adherents. But the fact is that the one strong church played a great part when it had a great part to play. That part is no longer called for, so that the one strong church is needed less. For hundreds of years it not only fought for its own existence but for the spiritual life of Europe. In times when the poorer classes were robbed of almost everything the church was their one defender. Viollet-le-Duc, the French architect and historian, tells us that the cathedrals were built by the peasants and burghers in protest against the nobles who were dotting the land with their strongholds. The cathedrals, according to him, were the result of tremendous popular movements in which the poor demanded something for themselves, and to keep it they put it under the protection of the Name of God. When times became more settled and the masses were left in peace to develop in their own way, the building of cathedrals ceased, and even those that had been begun were left uncompleted. The great mission of the one strong church was over. With peace, progress, expansion, prosperity, and the great spirit of adventure that woke when Vasco da Gama had found the way to the Indies, and Columbus had discovered America—with the invention of printing, the introduction of books, and the spread of knowledge above everything—the world entered on a new era, and among the first of the great forces of the old era to feel the change was the Church."

"Why?" Bobby asked simply.

"I think it was because it presented the religion of Christ from only one point of view, when, during all these hundreds of years, other points of view had been suppressed. They had been suppressed but they had not been eradicated. What we call the Reformation was to a large degree the forcing of these other points of view to the front. They were not new with Luther, Cranmer, John Knox, and their other exponents. They had been nursed in the hearts of men for centuries, but with the urgency of the one strong church to be as strong as possible there was no way of giving them efficient utterance. The man who did give them utterance became a heretic, and I think the reason why the heretic was held as the most terrible of all sinners was that he weakened the whole line of the Church in her attitude of defense. The Church couldn't afford to have heretics. She needed the whole field for herself. As soon as that field ceased to be a field of battle, from the very melting away of her ancient enemies, the heretic could assert himself. It was a question of taking off the pressure. When the Church no longer had her back to the wall, fighting against kings and emperors, she could do without the strictest policing of the Inquisition. Heretics not only lived; they flourished; they swarmed; they got possession of half the governments and churches in Europe."

It being necessary to explain to Bobby what a heretic was, he seized the main idea quickly.

"What was really happening was that the people who saw the religion of Christ differently from the way in which the one strong church had seen it were beginning to win recognition. That a great many people had been thinking along lines they had never dared to say anything about soon became evident. Among them were many of the clergy and of the monastic orders. I believe that this was specially the case in England, where the clergy led and the people followed. In other countries the people led, and the clergy hung back. But whichever way it was the old church was re-formed or a new church was created to set forth ideas which were considered new, but were really old ones long suppressed. When the great storm of the Reformation had cleared away there was at least this to the good, as I understand the good, that those who could not accept the one set of accretions to the teaching of Christ had the choice of another and even of a third and a fourth, so that they were free to cut themselves down to the simplest forms possible."

Bobby having asked what accretions were, his mother explained to him.

"You asked me," his father said to him, "what a church was for, and why we had so many of them. I said we had not so many of them, when you came to think of it. The Reformation left us with four new versions of what the one strong church had taught from its own angle. We had an English Church, a Scotch Church, a German Church, and a French Huguenot Church. Each stood for something which its adherents believed to be essential to the teaching of Christ. I can't go into what it was because that would involve us in too much doctrine and church history. But each stood for what a great many people believed with their whole souls. That is its justification, and a very complete justification I think it is. Since the Reformation three or four other strong churches have been formed, each embodying some principle which, it seems, the others have neglected. To me they exemplify the richness of Christianity, not a self-contradictory element within its teachings. I suppose a day may come when all their differences will be reconciled, but we are very far from it yet. At present the church system is the best we have been able to contrive."

While Leroy paused to redirect his thought Mabel stitched pensively, and Bobby stared, adoring his father the more for these ideas so far above his own head that he could catch only a dropped feather of one as it flew. Leroy had really more or less forgotten Bobby in his zeal to interest his wife in subjects becoming more and more vital to himself. When he continued his tone had altogether changed.

"And yet," he said slowly, as if thinking hard, in bringing out his words, "as a matter of fact, I don't see that what I have just called the church system has ever been successful from the start. It doesn't *work*. It never did work. Ever since Constantine let it out of the catacombs into the light of day the Church has been in trouble. To me she seems like a magnificent ship that has been built with a flaw in her construction, always pitching and rolling and running foul of other craft. It isn't only that she makes outside enemies—that is natural enough—but her quarrels within herself have always been extremely ugly ones. She seems to have had the faculty of breeding fanatics. Never was that more apparent than among certain of the churches in the United States in

this Twentieth Century which calls itself enlightened. More than once within two or three
years we have seen the most holy teachings of
the churches made scandalous by becoming
topics for the news sheet, with headlines to
rival those of the latest hold-up or notorious
divorce. Even apart from fanaticism each
church is at variance with every other. No one
of them recognizes otherwise than grudgingly
that any of the others has the same right to
exist that it has itself, while the old church of
the strong arm denies that right to them all. To
people not members of any church they are all
alike curiously unattractive. At the same time
they are all boastful, vainglorious, and sometimes a little untruthful. Listen to them shout-
ing:

> " 'We are not divided,
>   All one body we,
>   One in hope and doctrine,
>   One in charity,'

and you will get a defiance of the truth so fla-
grant that its very naïveté makes you laugh.

That any one of them was Christ's idea I find it difficult to believe. *He* founded something else."

Mabel dropped her sewing. "So you've said already. But, my dear Chris, what can you mean?"

"I mean something that the gospels are full of, and that everybody seems to miss. It is so incorporeal that even the saints and apostles seem to have missed it like the rest of us. At any rate, they acceded to a visible corporation —often suggesting that Church of the Kingdoms of This World and The Glory of Them which He Himself had rejected—as expressing the Christ-ideal, when He had been holding up to them this beautiful thing, without walls beyond the effort to do right, and no door but Himself."

"But what can it be?" Mabel asked in bewilderment. "I don't know much about religion, but I'm sure I never heard of it."

"Oh, yes, you have, only you've passed it by like everyone else. It was what He proclaimed when He first proclaimed anything."

"Well, what was that?"

"It was not, 'Repent ye, for the Church is at hand.' It was, 'Repent ye, for the Kingdom of Heaven is at hand.' "

Mabel looked disappointed, as if she had been expecting something more dramatic. "Oh, the Kingdom of Heaven! Rather far away, isn't it?"

"That's exactly what to Him it was not. It was at hand. It was here. It was open to everyone. It was the condition of everyone's welfare. Its access was the simplest possible. When you knew you were in it you were in it. The single condition of entry was to repent. That is to say, if you had not been trying to obey God and keep His commandments—which simply means trying to do right—you had to begin. You had to begin with the intention that as far as you could you would do God's will on earth as it is done in heaven. You had to understand heaven as not a place but the consciousness of the presence of God, and try to make your conduct harmonize with that. To this you added the knowledge that you were in Christ's special kingdom, and that He was your special king. In proportion as you could accomplish that, God's will was done for you as it is done in heaven. That is, you made a heaven of earth. You didn't postpone the Kingdom of Heaven till after you were dead. You entered it now; you entered it at will. You didn't have to ask any one about it, or apply for permission. It could be quite a secret thing between God and yourself, so long as you were sincere."

Bobby followed this with enough understanding to ask: "But what good did it do you?"

"It did you all the kinds of good you needed. I can express this only in general terms because those are all the Bible affords us; but we can see for ourselves that in this kingdom, as far as it was put into practice, all our wants were taken care of. We might say that temporal needs come first, for among the first things we are told of Him is that 'He taught the gospel of the Kingdom,' and healed all manner of disease. When He first sent out His twelve apostles their mission was to 'preach that the Kingdom of Heaven was at hand,' helping people in the most practical ways, in return for which they received the most practical protection. The inference is that within the Kingdom the first cares relieved are our temporal cares. Seek ye first the Kingdom of God, and then these common everyday needs will be met. Spiritual needs will become clearer when material wants are out of the way."

Mabel was interested. "But how much is there in the New Testament about this Kingdom?"

"Where He is the speaker a great deal. When He disappears there is less. Toward the latter part of the New Testament the idea seems to be dropped altogether. I can't help the feeling that it was too spiritual for them. They needed a visible corporation, and meetings which would have a certain social quality. As time went on the Church of the Kingdoms of this World and their Glory, with the controversies it engendered, blotted the conception out. But there it is for any reader of the New

Testament to see and, if he likes, to enjoy. At
any rate, to Jesus of Nazareth it was very dear.
It was the one thing of which He talked inces-
santly. If we may use the expression of Him,
it was a passion with Him. When alone with
His apostles 'the mysteries of the Kingdom of
Heaven' were His constant theme. All His rhe-
toric, all His imagination, all the immense
suggestions of His sympathy, He spent in re-
vealing the Kingdom as a power, a treasure,
a possession, a refuge, a place of escape from
the too-pressing ills of this world, and open to
all with a thought and a good intention. It was
as King of this Kingdom that He went to His
death. 'Art thou a king then?' Pilate asks, in
cynical pity. Jesus answers with proud humil-
ity: 'Thou sayest—that I am a King.' "

It was Bobby who put the question: "But,
Father, what's become of that Kingdom now?"

"It's still here, I suppose. It wasn't a tem-
porary thing. A Kingdom of God must be an
eternal condition. And—" he paused a minute
to consider—"I sometimes wonder if it isn't
some day going to prove our great way out."

"Out of what, Father?"

"Out of our religious perplexities. The churches seem to have given us all they have, and to leave us still unsatisfied. Thousands, millions, never go to a church. Thousands, millions, who do go, go and come away empty. The churches themselves often seem to me either swollen with self-complacency, or at their wits' ends to make the religion of Christ an "attraction," as the theatre is an attraction, or the motion picture play. But all over the world, among Catholics and Protestants alike, you'll find that there are people heartsick with longing for something to satisfy their spiritual need, and who never think of what Jesus taught us first of all. But it would not surprise me if some day they did, and found the Kingdom of Heaven what it was to Him—the heart's home."

CHAPTER V

WHAT IS A SACRAMENT?

IT WAS the midsummer holidays before Bobby asked another of his questions. When it came it was one Leroy was not expecting and was therefore not prepared for. Moreover, a long period had gone by with no further evidence of the lad's curiosity on religious subjects, and Leroy had begun to suppose that the interest had been dispelled by something else, as is so often the case in boyhood.

Bobby had asked the question at a moment opportune for his father since it was easy to postpone answering it. They happened to be galloping abreast on one of the shady bridle paths running through their own and the neighbouring properties. Ellie on her pony was in front with the groom, her mother slightly behind her, while the father and Bobby took their a sign that whatever Christ's standard is you want to be faithful to it. And just as the Roman soldier renewed his oath, or *sacramentum,* from time to time, the Christian does the same through certain specified rites. When all is said and done in criticism of the Christian Church, or any church in particular, it still remains true that it stands for a great tradition. Loyalty to that tradition must mean much in our lives, even when we don't fully agree with it or understand it. It has been the greatest force for good mankind has ever known, and though it might have been a greater force, it has been better than anything else. I come to feel more and more that it is an unwise thing to break with it, even though I have done so myself."

"Why did you, Father?"

"Because I was puzzled, and considered that being puzzled by some things was a reason for chucking everything. That's why I've been trying to impress on you that to do so is a foolish, callow act which in the end you may be sorry for. Truth is the biggest thing we have

been given to work out, and we can't work it out
in a few thousand years. Our minds are not
capable of that, yet each generation contributes
something toward the end. What we need is
first patience with ourselves for our slow
progress, and then patience with the other fellow because his progress is as slow as ours. As
it is, you might say that the scientist, the theologian, the historian, and the philosopher all
despise each other more or less, because they
work in different fields. As a matter of fact,
each is discovering his own little bit of truth
and is entitled to make mistakes while doing
it. Science, for instance, which in the Twentieth
Century speaks with so much proud assurance,
is one long story of error, and much of what
it is teaching to-day will be reversed again ten
years hence. Philosophy is always tinkering at
its old theories and turning them into new ones.
The historian lasts a generation or so, and then
goes out of date because of new light on old
subjects. Yet all of them add something to our
knowledge while they themselves are under-
going persistent change. And so it is with the

own pace in the rear. Bobby, who had been exploring a bypath recently opened up, had rejoined the party, and after galloping for some minutes side by side with his father, had shot his question from a sky clear of all such ideas.

"Father, what's a sacrament?"

Leroy was so little expecting such a question there and then that he smiled in surprise. Besides that, he didn't know—or he didn't know exactly. While he could have called back an answer of some sort, even there in the saddle, he preferred to seize the chance of putting the discussion off till he could talk of it with more intelligence.

"I think we'd better wait till we get home, my boy, before we go into that."

But at home Bobby's first business was to take a bath, and to change to the juvenile evening suit his mother insisted on his wearing now that he dined with his father and herself. Leroy, too, had similar duties, but before he performed them he hurried to the library to read the Encyclopædia Britannica article entitled "Sacrament" before Bobby could bring

up the topic again. The article brought back
to him details he had learned in boyhood, while
it stirred his mind to new suggestions. That sort
of stirring was easy, since, had he been given
to self-analysis—which he was not—he might
have said of himself what Rachel the actress
said of her master, Samson: "He gives me ideas
which give me ideas of my own." In ideas of
his own Leroy was fertile. They might not always be correct, but they were nearly always
challenging; and if they were too independent
to commend themselves widely they were at
least the product of a mind both frank and
reverent. Now that, for the sake of his boy, he
had come back to religion as the bond which
holds the disordered elements of life together
he wished to do so with deep respect for it as
conventionally taught. At the same time he
knew that his temperament would never allow
of his being enslaved by the conventions. He
was too free. He regarded too jealously the
freedom of others. The religion of Christ was
expressed for him not by a church but by a
teaching. That teaching he held as so simple

and clear as to require no interpretation by
authority. Where points were obscure they
were not important. He who ran could read.
What was really difficult and required explanation were the extensions of Christ's teaching
elaborated by the church at large or by any
one of the churches.

These he was anxious to respect even when
he found himself unable to accept them. If he
recognized in himself a right to criticize he
found no right to contradict. Those who had
given their teachings to the world only after
beating out the various subjects with prayer,
meditation, and intellectual power were much
more likely to be right than he with his un-
fledged judgments; and yet there he was with
a mind to think, and with thoughts that for
himself had some of the force of conviction.
What then was he to do? Inevitably he got
into situations inconsistent with himself; but
between inconsistency and a tampering with his
own sincerity the former was the lesser ill.

The Encyclopædia article, brief as it was,
had contained all the teaching on the subject

which he had once known and partly forgotten, with something more. The something more was chiefly historical, but extremely significant. As he bathed and changed his clothes he found new suggestions forming themselves, so that he could take up the subject with Bobby without a sense of absolute stupidity.

Smoking his after-dinner cigar he found himself alone with his son on the screened-in veranda furnished like an outdoor sitting room. Bobby played with Nosey, the wire-haired terrier, and Biddy, the old Irish setter, kept jealously poking her nozzle between them. Not till he had tired of this game and let the dogs out for a run in the growing darkness did Leroy find the opportunity to say:

"What made you ask me that question about sacraments this afternoon?"

Bobby replied indirectly. "When I was staying at Uncle Charlie's Aunt Agnes said that Peter had been confirmed and made his first Communion. She said it was a pity I couldn't have the same advantages."

"And what did you say to that?"

"I said I thought we had confirmation and Holy Communion in our church just the same as in theirs. I know that some of the boys at Doolittle's were confirmed last year, and went to the Communion too."

"But I suppose Aunt Agnes said that that was not the same thing."

"Yes, she said it wasn't the same thing at all. She said that you couldn't be really confirmed unless you were confirmed in their church, or receive the Communion either. Peter told me, too, that he'd been to confession, and would have to go once in so often from now on."

Leroy reflected. "You know Peter pretty well, don't you?"

"Pretty well; yes."

"And knowing him so well, and seeing him so often, have you noticed any difference in him since he was confirmed and made his first Communion?"

Bobby pondered. "Do you mean do I find him any better?"

"That's what it would come to."

"I haven't noticed much; but——"

"Try to notice now. He used to swear a good deal, didn't he? Does he swear less?"

Bobby hesitated. Since going to Doolittle's he had discovered that among boys there was a code of which one of the rules was against betraying another fellow to his elders or your own. But this was his father from whom he had never had any secrets, and with whom he was in the habit of discussing anything and everything as it came up. Peter was Uncle Charlie's and Aunt Agnes's grandson. You could perhaps speak of the members of your own family and their sins when it would be "tattling" to do it about non-relatives. He said, therefore, but with some reluctance: "No; he swears worse."

Of Peter, Leroy said no more. When he spoke it was to break in from another angle.

"Those fellows who you say were confirmed at Doolittle's last year. Are they still there?"

Bobby replied that they were.

"Do you know them well?"

"Middling well."

"And do you find them—how shall I put it?—influences for good in the school?"

Bobby hesitated again. "I don't want to tell you their names," he said at last.

"I don't want to know them."

"Well, then, one of them is all right. You mightn't call him an influence for good, but then he isn't an influence for anything. But the other two—well, they're about the limit."

Leroy said no more. This contradiction had always been one of his perplexities in confronting acts of religion. He, too, had been at Doolittle's. He, too, had been confirmed while there, and had received the Holy Communion. He remembered a few days, perhaps a week, during which he and his chums, who had gone through these rites together with himself, had been overawed by their solemnity, after which, as they expressed it, "the fun broke out again." The wildest and fastest set in the school they soon forgot that they were supposed to have "received grace" to enable them to lead another kind of life. He recalled now the fellows who

had made up what in those days they had called
"the gang." Two or three of them had become
respectable members of professions, husbands
and fathers. One was a churchwarden. But on
the other hand, two had died of alcoholism; one
had committed suicide after a long period of
embezzlement; one had been the hero of a
series of scandalous divorces; and so the list
went on. It was easy to recall dozens of other
fellows whom he had known less intimately
of whom similar things had been true. They
had been duly admitted to the sacraments, but
as far as human judgment could follow them
no particle of grace had ever descended upon
them. The same thing had been true of himself, so true that he had been driven to wonder
if after all there were not something in Aunt
Agnes's assertions that outside her own church
the sacraments had no validity. And yet there
were his cousins, Aunt Agnes's own sons, whom
he knew to the core, leading much the same life
that he led himself, and here was young Peter
apparently on the way to follow their example.
On the other hand, there was Bobby, who had

Church. Each one of its many movements may be said to advance us a little toward truth; but it takes time. It may take many centuries. From one point of view the advance of the human race is slow, since it has taken us something like six thousand years to work up from the prehistoric to where we are to-day; and yet when you consider the millions of years it has taken to produce most physical changes six thousand years is very little. That, I presume, is due to our possession of reason, which has enabled us to go more rapidly; and during all the time that reason has been active man's spiritual power has been active too. Only like every other faculty it has reached what it knows of truth through error or mistake. The Bible is the history of the way in which the spiritual faculty learned how not to do it. When it gives us a man who 'did it' perfectly it stops. There was no further need of its going on. But, as I said before, it took time, and time called for patience."

"And you mean," Bobby said astutely, "that

they call for time and patience still, don't
you?"

"Yes, and for loyalty. Loyalty is never so
much in demand as when people are in trouble.
The Church is in great trouble. Everyone
seems to have a stick or a stone to pelt her with.
She's always been persecuted, of course, but
just now the persecution is the more annoying
because much of it is so petty. It comes from
millions of people who do exactly what I've
done myself; first they desert her and then
they speak ill of her. I'll admit that she tempts
one to speak ill of her. There never, it seems
to me, was an institution that so provoked one's
ill temper. It's so cocksure on the subject of
possessing the final truth. Each church is as
cocksure as every other, while all of them must
be suspected of at least some insincerity. And
yet we have nothing that can take the Church's
place, nor are we likely to have for thousands
of years to come. Imperfect as she is, ridiculous
as she sometimes appears to many of us, she
still represents the highest ideals we've been
able to attain to. A sacrament, then, is in a way

an oath of loyalty to the best things that men know anything about."

Bobby asked his question with the directness of youth. "Well, Father, are you and Mother going to be loyal to them now?"

Leroy answered this as frankly as he could. "I'm trying to find a way. In all the churches there's so much I dislike that I'm looking for a compromise. I don't want merely to go back, and sit in a pew, and listen to a sermon, and come away half grudging the time I've spent. I want to do the thing whole-heartedly, and till I can feel that I'm doing so I'd better think and look about me."

There was still, however, something to say about sacraments which he thought he had better explain while he had the opportunity. This was partly the historical side, which the Encyclopædia had given him, and partly that spiritual aspect which had been taught him as a boy, and which he found it so hard to reconcile with the facts of life as he had observed them. He told Bobby how the Church had gradually made rulings which defined a sacrament as a rite with more clear-cut limits than the faithful had hitherto ascribed to it, and reduced these rites in number. The one strong church had fixed that number as seven, two greater and five lesser. The two greater were of course baptism and the Holy Communion. Of the five lesser he would say nothing now, as it might confuse them. The church into which Leroy himself had been born, and which in his own phrase he had deserted, used a variant on this definition, declaring that there were but two sacraments, and five rites of a sacramental nature. The other churches used other variants still; but he presumed that most of them put baptism and Holy Communion in the forefront as the great essentials.

"The definition of a sacrament given me when I was your age was 'the outward and visible sign of an inward and spiritual grace.' That is, you brought your child to a font where water was poured on him and a certain sacred formula said over him. That was the outward and visible sign, and was accompanied by a supply of grace which made the infant a mem-

ber of the Church, a child of God, and an in-
heritor of the kingdom of heaven." Expecting
Bobby to ask why he himself had never been
baptized, a subject which the father was not
yet ready to discuss, Leroy hurried on. "The
outward and visible sign in the Holy Communion is the reception of bread and wine,
taken as representing the Body and Blood of
Christ, after which comes the grace of a physical or spiritual—I can never understand
which they mean—union with our Lord."

Once more Bobby's question surprised his
father, who welcomed it rather than another,
because it was a theme he himself liked to reflect on. "But, Father, what do they mean by
grace?"

"I'm glad you've asked me that, even though
I can't quite explain it to you. I have a feeling
that I can't explain it for the reason that it's
not quite explainable. It's something to feel,
to thrill to, to love, and which nevertheless can't
easily be put into words." He paused in order
to express himself simply. "In the first place,
it's one of the most lovely words in any lan-

guage. You might say that grace is the highest
element in beauty. To possess grace is perhaps
to possess beauty in the form in which it is
most lasting. Your mother, for instance, would
not be called a beautiful woman, but she's an
extremely graceful one. That charm she will
probably never lose as long as she lives. It was
a curious instinct that made some of the later
writers of the Old Testament express the gifts
of God by this term of beauty. Still more curious was it that the writers of the New Testament, who had probably little of what we call
the æsthetic sense, should have seized on this
exquisite word to indicate God's chief working in the soul. Grace brought strength as its
natural consequence. True grace, you know, is
always strong. Of one of the most graceful
women of the Nineteenth Century, the
Empress Eugénie, it used to be said that she had
the strength that comes when every muscle
and fibre is in exactly the right place. In a
general way you might consider grace as almost synonymous with strength. But it is
strength combined with beauty, and it is beauty

of the spirit rather than of the flesh. What beauty of the spirit means we can hardly say, because our faculties, which are mainly of the senses, know so little of what spirit is. St. Paul says that spiritual things are spiritually discerned, and I suppose that we must leave it at that. Otherwise we fall into the futile error of what George Eliot calls putting on spectacles to discern odours."

In the silence that followed it occurred to Leroy that that was what he himself had been doing. In his judgments on those who had received the sacraments he had been trying to appraise the degree of grace which had come to them when he had no capacity for measuring it. He saw what they did externally, but he couldn't see the action of the Holy Ghost within them. Even with the two chaps who had died of alcoholism and the embezzler who had committed suicide there was doubtless some action of the spirit of grace which passed in a world beyond his ken. In his very self this action might be beyond his ken. He had received those "means" by which the church into which he had been born assure him that grace had been given him, and he had doubted the fact because he hadn't felt it. That is, he had put on his spectacles to discern odours. He had tried to test spiritual things by sensuous weights. That beautiful thing called grace, which seemed to him as if it must be the same as the Holy Ghost, might easily have been with him all this time, waking an impulse, a bit of remorse, a longing desire, till now, with Bobby's young life to guide . . .

But Bobby, who had been thinking on his own account, changed the current of his father's thought. "I suppose, Father, that that oath which the soldiers took, that *sacramentum,* had no connection with the oaths people use to-day, not in courts, I don't mean, but in talking."

"What we call profanity?"

Bobby nodded. Leroy was glad the boy had broached the topic of his own accord, since he had long wished to speak to him about it.

"On the contrary; it has a very close connection indeed. What we call a sacrament is

our effort to repeat and to honour our oath of
loyalty to Jesus Christ—it is something more,
but it is that in the first place—whereas what
we understand as profanity is the attempt to
degrade it. There was a time when I looked
on a profane oath as just a word by which the
speaker meant no harm. When I was at college
I was rather profane myself, and I'll tell you
what disgusted me with the habit. One of these
days it may disgust you, if you take the same
business training as I took. After I had left
college my father sent me into one of our factories; and in order to learn all about the business I began at the bottom. Of the thousand
men and women who worked there not more
than fifty knew who I was. In that way I saw
people just as they were and heard them talk.
Well, the talk horrified me. I'd heard some
good round swearing in college, and some filth
into the bargain; but it was clean in comparison with what you heard shouted all over the
place. It wasn't done merely by the hands, because if anything the heads of the departments

were the worst. They had a custom with a poor worker—and even with a good worker if they didn't like him—of 'bawling him out.' I've been bawled out myself by someone who didn't know who I was. And then you heard the blasphemy, the foulness, the absolute rottenness, of which the English language is capable. The women, of whom we always employed a couple of hundred, had to listen to it as well as the men. Sometimes it was used *at* them; but they had to take it as if they didn't hear it, bowing their heads and blushing. When I spoke to my father about it, naming this man or that, often someone high up in the business, he would only sigh and say, 'Yes, I know; but he's too valuable a man for me to interfere with. I couldn't do without him.' When I moved to another of our factories I found the same thing. In the army it was worse. I remember one time . . . but I try not to soil my mind with the recollection. And when I came to analyze it all this is what I found."

Bobby, who had lost so much of what his father said because it was too advanced for him, understood this and followed with close attention. Leroy began again after a slight pause.

"Of the terrible obscenities I shall say nothing because I'm ashamed even to refer to them. But there is a form of profanity which is not so much obscene as it is blasphemous. And there we find the evil of what we might call plain ordinary swearing. You'll notice it always concerns itself with our deepest and most sacred mysteries. 'God!' 'God Almighty!' 'Christ Almighty!' 'Jesus Christ!' These are our favourite oaths, often accompanied by foul words which make the blasphemy itself more shocking. When it doesn't profane our dearest things it turns to the most terrible: devils, damnation, hell. This is, of course, nothing new in our history. As long ago as the time of Joan of Arc the English were known in France as *les Goddams*. But I think it has been left to us altogether to defile the spirit of the ancient *sacramentum* till the names of God and Jesus Christ seem to have hardly any use but the horrible. In one of our factories I tried to learn whether any religion or race took the lead in this profanation; but I couldn't discover that any one was to blame more than any other. Catholics, Protestants, and Jews alike were so foul mouthed that they kept each other in countenance. The foreigner soon caught up with the American. You'll probably yourself have to face it some day, and I shall feel as if I were sending you into a bath of dirt."

Bobby's face grew more manly, and at the same time the more innocent. "But, Father, if I'm loyal to the *sacramentum*——"

"When you take it."

"Oh, but I've taken it already—to myself."

As Nosey and Biddy came scratching at the door Leroy rose to admit them, but he could not resist the impulse to put his arm over the boy's shoulder, and press his head against him, as he passed.

CHAPTER VI

WHAT IS BAPTISM?

"DEAR MR. LEROY:

"*Will you allow me to come and see you and Mrs. Leroy sometime in the near future when you are quite alone? A most singular thing has happened which I should like to talk over with you confidentially. If it was on a day when your children were not in the house, or at least could be kept from the knowledge that I had come, it would be so much the better.*

"*Yours sincerely,*

"RUPERT OAKES."

The note was dated from the parsonage of the church opposite. In preparation for Bobby's return to the Doolittle School the family had now come back to the house in town. Having read this communication, Leroy passed it to his wife.

"But what can it mean?" she asked in astonishment. "What can Bobby and Ellie have been up to?"

"I presume that that's what he wants to tell us."

A date having been fixed with Mr. Oakes, the children were sent, to get them out of the way, to lunch with their Aunt Susie. The clergyman proved to be a tall, spare, ascetic-looking man, a gentleman, and a Harvard graduate. The social preliminaries being over he plunged into his subject at once.

"At our week-day service on Friday afternoon, when the congregation was sparse and scattered, I was surprised to see in one of the front pews a handsome, manly boy, holding by the hand a pretty little girl who looked frightened by the strangeness of the place. They were clearly unused to the service, sitting still and taking no part in it. When it was over and the congregation gone they were still in the same place as I came out of the vestry. Naturally, I went up to speak to them, and they both rose. Then, as they still held hands, this is the conversation, as nearly as I can remember, that took place. The boy asked me if I was the clergyman of the church, to which I replied that I was. 'Do you baptize people?' he asked me next, and I said I did. 'Would you baptize my sister and me?' was his next question, whereupon I asked him what made him think of it. To this he answered that almost everyone was baptized, and he thought he and his sister ought to be so, too. 'I'm at the Doolittle School in Connecticut,' he added, 'and I think I'm the only unbaptized boy they've got. There may be another one or two, but I don't believe so. Besides—' and then he went on to say the oddest thing I ever heard in my life—'besides, I want to take the *sacramentum*. I've taken it already to myself, but I want to do it in the regular way, and out loud. I've told my sister about it, and she wants to take it, too.' Though I was amazed I tried not to let him see it, because he was so much in earnest, and so honest. I asked him what he meant by the *sacramentum,* to which he replied that he meant the oath the soldiers of Christ took to be loyal to Him and the Church. He went on to say that his father had told him about it, and would be glad to have him do it. 'Do it when?' 'Right now—this afternoon,' was his answer. 'We're both ready, aren't we, Ellie?' Naturally, I wanted to know then who his father was and where he lived, so he told me. The upshot of it was that I said I couldn't baptize them then and there, but that I would think it over and talk to them again. They seemed disappointed, but they made no objection when I led them down to the entrance, and watched them cross the street to go in at your own door. I said nothing as to coming to see you about it, but I thought it proper to do so; and I should like to add that I don't think I ever saw so prepossessing a boy."

Of this incident the first result was that Leroy laid in every book and article he could find that would tell him something about baptism. He didn't know the day or hour when Bobby would spring the topic. He had still two weeks before returning to school, so that his opportunities would be many. And yet the time passed and Bobby, falling into one of those spells of reticence to which boys are subject, was altogether silent. Not till he came home again for the Christmas holidays did he say anything about it. Even then he confessed to nothing connected with his visit to Mr. Oakes, but contented himself with asking one day, when both his father and mother were present, why he couldn't be baptized.

"What's put that into your head?" his father asked, as if the idea was new to him.

Bobby replied that everyone was, that as far as he could judge there was not a boy in the school who had not been baptized as a kid, with the exception of two fellows who attended the Baptist Church, and had not been baptized on principle. "Why wasn't I done as a kid, Father, and Ellie, too? You were, and so was Mother. Then we should be like everybody else."

Having perhaps grown too shy, he said nothing about the *sacramentum,* his whole emphasis being laid on conformity to what seemed a general custom, at least in the society into which he had been born. His mother made the explanation he was asking for.

"We did think of having you done when you were a baby; but it happened just then that we went to two christenings which we didn't like. One was your Aunt Susie's little girl, who died not long afterward, and the other of your cousin, Peter. In both churches they seemed to consider that the poor innocent little baby was a creature born in sin, out of whom the devil had to be cast before it could be saved; and that rather disgusted us. When Ellie came along we felt the same thing.

"I'm not sure now," the father added, "that it wasn't a mistake. In both cases the thought and language are mediæval; but once a church gets that sort of thing fastened on it, it's not so easy to get rid of it. You can't be changing your formulas—and you always need *some* formulas —to suit the opinions of every new generation, so that the best thing seems to be to let them stand and interpret them to suit yourself. Personally, I should hesitate now to break with the great and ancient tradition of the Church, even though I didn't wholly agree with the implications of its phraseology."

"That means," Bobby ventured, in his own tongue, "that if I was a little kid now you'd have me done—the way you've come to think. Well, why can't I be done as it is? Then I'd be like every other boy."

"Unfortunately, you're not a little kid," the father objected, "and I don't think you should be done now without your knowing something more about it. By the way, how much do you know?"

"I don't know anything except what you told me, that it's the *sacramentum* by which I swear to be loyal to the best things we know anything about. I ought to do that, oughtn't I? Anyhow, it's what I want to do."

"My goodness!" Mabel exclaimed, "where did you hear that? I didn't know it myself."

"Father told me, when we were in the country in the summer."

Leroy felt apologetic. "It was one evening when you weren't there. Bobby had asked me what a sacrament was, and so I explained it to him as well as I could."

"Chris, dear, they ought to make you a

bishop. If it was an archbishop or a cardinal it wouldn't be good enough, at the pace you're taking."

"You're the great objection to my being made a cardinal, dear. A cardinal must always be a celibate." To Bobby he added: "Some day before you go back to school we'll talk it all out, and I'll tell you about baptism the little that I know."

"All right, Father; that's a promise, and I'll keep you to it."

But they dropped into the discussion by accident. Bobby having come on the following Sunday to the luncheon table without having washed his hands was scolded by his mother, while he did his best to defend himself. He had not washed his hands because they were already clean, and to wash them to no purpose was not only silly but would have obliged him to climb two flights of stairs to his own room. His mother argued that it was not wholly a question of cleanliness, but of proper deference to those with whom you sat down to a meal.

Partly because his recent reading had filled

his mind with the subject, and partly to keep the family peace, Leroy threw in: "Like the ceremonial washings of the ancients. They were forever washing, whether they were clean or not. All ancient literatures, both Hebrew and Gentile, are full of ablutions and lustrations, and we know from their ruins that some of their baths were stupendous."

"I know what ablutions are," Mabel said, in her cool, satiric tone, "but I must say I never heard of lustrations."

"Ablutions were of course washings for the sake of cleanliness, and were generally in obedience to their sanitary laws. They needed such laws, and they needed such ablutions. Their climates were generally warm; their clothing light; their getting about for the most part on foot over dusty roads. Either they went barefooted, or they wore sandals which though healthier than our modern shoes were not so much of a protection. Bathing facilities must have been abundant. To read the Book of Leviticus you would suppose that a large part of the population must have spent their time in bathing their persons and washing their clothes. It was really not much wonder that their wealth was largely put into changes of raiment."

"Yes, that was ablutions; but you haven't yet told us what lustrations were," Mable insisted.

"Ablutions and lustrations were outwardly much the same thing, but in each the motive was slightly different. Ablutions were dictated by taste, custom, or the simple reason that you needed a bath. The lustration had a religious motive behind it, and implied inner purification through an outward symbol. By the Gentile it was done in honour of some god; by the Hebrew as an outward and visible sign that he had expiated and been forgiven for some sin. A lustration among the Latins became a *baptisma* among the Greeks, from whom the later Hebrews borrowed the word to express the many kinds of purification by water which their own religion imposed on them. When you come to think of it, purification by water was the most natural symbol either Jew or Gentile

could have chosen. The element could be pro-
cured anywhere; it cost nothing; and being the
means of outward cleanliness it suggested at
once that cleansing of the soul of which most
people at some time in their lives have felt the
need."

Bobby asked: "Well, wouldn't *baptisma* be
something like baptism?"

"It would be very like it. Baptism is in fact
the one vestige that remains to us of all these
laws and habits. It was undoubtedly because of
the many forms of baptism already in use that
it was adopted by Christ as a symbol of the
purification He so strongly urged. To repent
and be baptized was the substance of most of
the earliest preaching. It was not that the baptism in itself could do anything; but as the outward and visible sign of an inward and spiritual grace it was a witness to a spiritual process
going on within the soul. To repent came first;
everything depended on that; the washing
with water was no more than external evidence."

"But if you repented," Mabel objected, "I

don't see that the washing with water—the baptism—was strictly necessary."

"Perhaps it wasn't; but human nature is so constituted that it isn't content with what is purely inward and spiritual; it demands something that it can do externally. That's especially true of the ordinary run of people. All except the few but fit are dissatisfied without ceremonial. Some ceremonial runs through all our lives; but when we come to religion, which is so mysterious to us, and in general so little understood, ceremony becomes largely the means by which we venture to approach God. Protestantism has done something to abolish it; but even Protestants are never quite insensible to the movements, the lights, the colours, the genuflections, the prostrations, the tinkling of bells, the mystery, and the feeling of the coming and going of a God, which they get in the Greek and Roman churches. It may seem childish to them; and when you come to think of it, it *is* childish, in the sense of being primitive; but on the masses of us it is effective."

"But I should think that in your outward and

visible signs there would be a menace to what you call true religion."

"Of course! Ceremonialism leads to formalism, and formalism to no true religion at all, as surely as the years lead to death. That's the great danger that Protestantism has been fighting against for the last three hundred years. But Protestantism so often makes the mistake of being dreary and ugly that it defeats its own ends. Jesus of Nazareth seems to me to show His wisdom in allowing some symbolism but in making it the simplest and most familiar possible. There is no question but that He did associate the washing with water, in other words baptism, very closely with the essentials to His teachings."

"But it seems to me," Mabel put in, "that I've heard that baptism means a lot of things besides just a symbol of purification."

"So it does, but not as many as the Greeks and Latins tried to make it mean. We must remember that all our Christianity comes to us filtered through that sieve. The Hebrews had finished their task with the Christian religion when the New Testament had been written. Everything else, all that comes to us from the early Christian writers, is a Greek and Latin version of what was taught by Jesus Christ and the apostles, and is intensely coloured by the interpretation. Greeks and Latins alike were tremendous talkers. They not only discussed everything and all the time, but they discussed subtly, and with a good deal of the fanciful. They were not afraid of the fanciful, nor of the involved. They were not even afraid to infuse into their explanations an element of the magical. The magical was very near them. The majority of those by whom they were surrounded believed in it; many of them had believed in it themselves. We should never forget that most of the early Christians, even the wisest and holiest, had lived in such an atmosphere of superstition that it was impossible to human nature to eradicate it all at once. True, we look back to them as saints and authorities, and in some ways so they were; but they were never so much so that they couldn't go in for the Greco-Latin hairsplitting which was so

dear to them. In that they revelled, and never
did they revel in it with more glee than when
they got hold of a symbolic subject like baptism into which they could read dozens of
meanings which were not there."

"And did they agree?"

"Of course they didn't agree. Each Father
of the Church laid stress on what appealed to
himself, so that the early generations of Christians were more controversial even than we
are to-day. The plain fact is that by the time
two or three hundred years had separated
them from the Apostolic Age they knew far less
about it than we do at the present time. History
was not yet written; scholarship hadn't been
born; to a large extent the faculty of faithful
oral tradition had been lost through the increase of population and the greater sophistica-
tion. The teaching of Christian doctrine was
to no inconsiderable extent a matter of go-as-
you-please, till the one strong church of which
we've already spoken rose to impose its authority. Then, with a few commanding figures
like St. Augustine to support it, something like

unanimity of opinion could prevail. On the subject of baptism Augustine is supposed to have laid down the law; but that it was not laid down very definitely we can see from the fact that at the present day Protestants and Catholics both trace back to him."

They went on with the conversation after they had risen from the table and gone into the library. Inevitably, the talk drifted into a discussion between Leroy and his wife rather than between father and son. In a way Leroy was more concerned that Mabel should get his points of view than Bobby, since what the parents both understood could the more easily be transmitted to the children.

"But that's getting into the realm of theology," he continued, after they had got seated, "which is what I specially don't want to do. In the first place it's very complicated, and in the second I know nothing about it. All I'm trying to find out is how much religion can be practically used by the common man."

"Well, then," came from Mabel, "suppose that Bobby and I are the common man, what do you yourself make out to be the meaning of baptism, and what is it that seems to make it so necessary to religious people? If you can put it into language that Bobby can understand we shall profit by it so much the more."

"I understand most of it as it is," Bobby protested; "at least I get the sense of it. It's only now and then that I don't."

"The history of baptism as it's given in the New Testament," Leroy began, after a spell of thinking, "seems to me fairly simple. The first we hear of it under its present name is when John the Baptist came to the banks of the river Jordan preaching the baptism of repentance for the remission of sins. It seems to have been one of those periods, which occurred every now and then, of great national tension. Their sins were uppermost in people's minds, and they needed the assurance which he gave them that all flesh should see the salvation of God. Multitudes came out to him, including the most despised elements of the populace, the tax gatherers and the soldiers who had traded themselves off to the Roman authority. When they confessed their sins he not only baptized them but gave them sound practical advice."

"Did he baptize them right there in the river?" Bobby asked.

"Yes, right there in the river. But in doing that he did nothing they considered strange. Their own many forms of the *baptisma* had accustomed them to the whole idea of purification by water, as practised from immemorial time by the nations whom they knew. The impression John made was so profound that all men mused in their hearts as to whether he could be the Christ or not, till he himself settled the question by assuring them that he was not. 'One mightier than I cometh,' he informed them. 'He shall baptize you with the Holy Ghost and with fire.' I should like you to notice that word fire, because it points to the purely figurative use of the element in which baptism was administered. He was not, of course, going to baptize with fire. As a matter of fact, He was not going to baptize at all, and never did. But just as water was a cleansing force, fire was even more so; and both were

wholly symbolical. Except for literal obedience to Christ's words I can conceive of a
purely spiritual baptism in which neither fire
nor water would be used; only that that would
be outside the ancient tradition to which I at
least would like to reunite myself if I only
saw a way."

"But, Father, *could* you have a baptism without water?"

"Not in the ordinary sense, no. Most of us
need the symbol. We can't imagine that the
Holy Ghost could come to us without it."

"The Holy Ghost?" Mabel said, in a tone of
inquiry. "Has He anything to do with it?"

"That was the difference, as I understand it,
between John's baptism and Christian baptism.
John's baptism was significant of the forgiveness of sins only. Christ's baptism symbolized
what they called power from on high. Grace—
spiritual strength—the Holy Ghost—I think
the common man can take them as meaning
much the same thing. The theologian, for aught
I know, may see them otherwise; but I'm trying to simplify it down to what people like our-

selves can understand. Much of the difference
that I see between the dispensation of the Old
Testament and that of the New is in this conception of power. Christ's idea of a man is that
of a being capable of doing things that would
amaze himself. This heightened spiritual
strength was the gift of the Holy Ghost, the
Working Force of God. This Working Force
comes to everyone in proportion as he is able
to receive it. Some are prepared to use much
of it; some less; some scarcely any of it; but
all are endowed with the capacity of receiving
at least a little. What it is we don't know, beyond the fact that it is what we call inspiration.
Not only is it inspiration in the abstract, but it
is given us for particular purposes. Everyone
who receives the Spirit receives it to make him
the more useful, one in a trade, one in a factory,
one in a profession, one as a teacher—you may
run the whole list of occupations—and all to
make themselves more spiritually strong in the
face of their many temptations."

"Do you mean," Mabel asked, "that baptism
brings all that with it?"

Leroy reflected. "Perhaps I shouldn't say
that baptism brought all that with it so much
as that it's the outward and visible sign that it
is there. I don't suppose that a few prayers and
a little water can summon the Holy Ghost.
That was the half-magical idea of the early
ages. The Holy Ghost must be wherever there
is life. There have been great men, great geni-
uses, great benefactors of mankind, who never
heard either of the Holy Ghost or of baptism,
but in whom the Working Force of God was
operative just the same. But what I mean is
that to us who *have* heard of both, and of a great
deal more besides, the outward and visible
sign comes as an assurance. It's in the first
place an assurance of purification, and then it's
an assurance of the constant renewal of our
depleted energies. When I was a small boy,
before I went to the Doolittle, I was for a
couple of years a choir boy in the church the
family attended. And in Lent we used to have
a service at which we sang to a noble Gregorian
chant the penitential psalm, the *Miserere*.
Well, one Lent I had a very guilty conscience

over something I'd been doing. Boys suffer from guilty consciences oftener than they're given credit for. And I still remember the brace I got from one of the verses of that psalm. I'd thought of myself as too bad ever to be forgiven; but this was the verse that bucked me up. 'O give me the comfort of thy help again, and stablish me with thy free spirit.' It was the word 'again' that did the trick for me. It was the first intimation I'd ever had that I *could* have the comfort of help again, let alone being stabilized by the free Spirit. That stayed by me for a number of years, till I got into college and chucked the whole thing. But it gives a very fair idea of what I'm trying to say. Baptism is a sign to me and to everyone else that we come to the Holy Ghost to be cleansed by water or by fire—the symbol is of secondary importance—and endowed with His perpetual help. How He gives me that help I don't know; neither do I know exactly what that help consists in. But I do know that it is the Divine Force that came to this world when the Spirit of God first moved on the face of the waters of chaos, and has never left it."

For a few minutes there was silence in the room till Mabel said: "Then if that is so, I can't see why you should baptize a baby, who can't understand anything about it."

Leroy was quick with his reply. "Did you ever see a baby that didn't need the Holy Ghost? I don't suppose that there's any time in the life of a human being when the supreme Working Force is more of a stimulus to him than at the beginning. What a child learns in the first two or three years is prodigious. Lying in his cradle, seemingly incapable of thought, his little mind is busily at work, observing, collating, coördinating, remembering, while he learns to distinguish between one person and another, gets the names and functions of the members of the family, the sounds of speech, the meanings of words, and surprises everyone after a few months by speaking a word himself. That in all this he should need the help of the Holy Ghost seems to me to go without saying."

"Then you think," Mabel said, as a question rather than a comment, "that if he hasn't been baptized he doesn't get it."

"Nothing would ever persuade me to believe anything of the kind," Leroy replied with emphasis. "I may neglect my child, but the Holy Ghost will not. I do not believe that the sweetest thing in all the world, a little baby, is 'conceived and born in sin,' even though ancient formulas say it is. I let them say so, and go on thinking my own thoughts. But I do believe that blame attaches to the parents who refuse or neglect to take their children into the great company of the purified and reborn. The Holy Ghost may see to it that the children themselves do not suffer; but I can't help the feeling that the parents may."

"Baptists don't think so," Bobby spoke up. "We've two Baptist fellows in the school, and they won't be baptized till they're grown men."

"The Baptists are a strong and sturdy-hearted people," Leroy replied, "and they've a right to their opinions. We who've taken baptism so erroneously, and often so light-

mindedly, should be the last to object to the
seriousness with which they hold their convic-
tions. They have their way of thinking and we
have ours. But for me," he added, so humbly
that he seemed ashamed, "I should like to see
both of my children born again of water and
the Spirit. Even though I've only the crudest
idea of the meaning of that phrase, I know it's
a good meaning, connected with the Working
Power of God, and that's enough for me."

Before Bobby went back to school both he
and Ellie were, as Mabel expressed it, "done."

CHAPTER VII

WHAT IS A MIRACLE?

THE first signs of skepticism on Bobby's part came during the following midsummer holidays, when he was fourteen. Before he was an hour in the house both father and mother had noticed a change in him. Somehow what Mr. Oakes, the clergyman, had called the prepossessing boy had disappeared. In his place had come a young hobbledehoy, rather noisy, more or less self-assertive, and a little patronizing toward his parents, his home, and his sister. The change was not so great that they could instantly point it out; they analyzed it only by degrees; and though in the atmosphere of the family some of it melted away, some of it remained. He was more independent, more detached. Leroy, in particular, felt pained that in this process of growing up he should inevitably become less adoringly affectionate; but as a father he knew that his beloved little boy, who had been used to hang caressingly about him and grow confidential, was gone forever.

As to religion he asked no more questions. Leroy himself, having become more and more deeply interested in the subject, had looked forward to perhaps several discussions with his son before the summer was ended; but Bobby gave no opening. At times the father guessed that he was a little ashamed of the interest he had displayed already.

It was almost autumn, and close to their return to town, before Bobby was sufficiently stirred to speak. It happened that some people, who had been hearing a sermon on the miracles of the New Testament, had come in to tea. Talking of this, there was between them no small difference of opinion. Some there were who discredited the miracles; some believed in them. Leroy said nothing, but he noticed the keenness with which Bobby followed now one speaker, now another. In the evening after dinner, as they sat with Mabel on the screened-in porch, Bobby broke his silence at last.

"Father, can't you believe in the Bible without believing in all those miracles? Nobody does them now."

For a minute or more Leroy smoked his cigar without answering. "That's the attitude a good many people take up," he said then, "but to me it's chiefly a question of authenticity. If you leave out the so-called miracles, you leave out a great part of the gospels. You still have a framework left, but it's not much more than a framework. It's like a portrait that's been so hacked that you can no longer recognize the face. To me the portrait given in the gospels is one of the most amazing things in all literature. I'm very sure that it hasn't a parallel elsewhere."

"In what way?" Mabel asked. "Just what do you mean?"

"I mean the extraordinary feat accomplished by four different men, working at different times, more or less independently of each other, with different objects in view, and drawing precisely the same Man. If we had only one of the four we should have that Man as clearly

put before us as we have Him now. While it
is probable that the later writers among them
had copies of what the earlier had done there
was nothing on their parts like collusion or co-
operation. They were too simple for that, too
unsophisticated. 'Ignorant and unlearned men,'
the Apostles are called by someone who knew
them, and if we except the author of the Gospel
According to St. John, so were the evangelists;
and yet they were equal to this marvellous ac-
complishment. When you think of the many accounts we have, let us say, of Queen Elizabeth,
or Mary Queen of Scots, or George Washing-
ton, given us by those who had seen more of
them than the evangelists ever saw of Jesus
Christ, and the differences, and often the con-
tradictions, between them all, what was done
by these ignorant and unlearned men becomes
the more amazing. Why," he continued, ad-
dressing Mabel directly, "if you, Bobby, and
I each undertook to give a description of Susie,
or of Uncle Charlie, or of anybody else whom
we know very well, we should have three char-
acters so diverse from each other that it would

be difficult to recognize them as meant for the same person. Take Abraham Lincoln, for example. There are as many Lincolns as there are writers who've described him, and many of them knew him well. But here the Jesus of Matthew is that of Mark; the Jesus of Luke is that of John. All these gospels differ considerably in intention; but the Man who is their inspiration remains the same. Even where there is some slight variation in detail, it is never anything that affects Him."

"Then," Mabel observed, "there *is* some variation?"

"Yes," Leroy admitted; "what I should call variation without conflict. Now and then one of them gives a detail which is what he remembers of a particular incident, while another of them may give another detail which may easily have been a component part of the same occurrence. The accounts of the Resurrection have, for example, to be pieced together and harmonized to make a fairly complete whole; but that, I think, isn't difficult to do. There's one point of view that very few of us remember;

that these are not biographies. The writing of
biography was not yet a literary form, though
a few ancient writers had attempted something
of the sort. Something of the sort is also done
sketchily in a number of the books of the Old
Testament; but a detailed account of a man's
life from the cradle to the grave hadn't yet
been conceived of. St. Luke, who seems to
have written not only his gospel but the Acts
of the Apostles as well, probably expresses to
his friend Theophilus, in the opening words
of the Acts, exactly what all four were trying
to do. Get me a Bible, Bobby, will you? and
I'll give you the very words." Bobby having
returned with a translation of the New Testament into modern speech, Leroy found the
place and read: " 'My former narrative,
Theophilus, dealt with what Jesus did and
taught *as a beginning.'* I can't think that any
of the evangelists attempt to do more than that.
Even that they put not so much into the form
of narrative as into that of notes. Did you ever
notice how short each of the gospels is? The
longest of them is scarcely more than what we

should call a pamphlet. Printed in the largest type in general use a New Testament is still a moderately small volume; and of that small volume the gospels are only a small part; and yet they set forth in perfect colour and line this stupendous character."

Mabel murmured something about this being true, though she had never thought of it.

"Moreover," Leroy went on, "it is the sort of thing which writers find most difficult. It's always easier to describe a man with plenty of human weaknesses than it is to make a convincing picture of a good one. Thackeray said that since Fielding wrote *Tom Jones* no English writer had dared describe a man. He meant that it had become impossible to depict in print the licentiousness not only of the individual but of the epoch; and yet, comparatively speaking, it was an easy thing to do. Everyone believes in licentiousness, and it requires no persuasion or hard work to make the imagination reproduce it. No one believes in perfection as a human characteristic, and when Tennyson tried to show it in his Arthur of the

Idylls of the King he was very quickly ridiculed except by the over-sentimental. But these men, with no art whatever, incapable of writing correctly the language they were using, make a perfect human being credible. Not only that but they make Him the most credible human being ever drawn. Neither Sophocles, nor Shakespeare, nor Goethe, nor any other among our greatest dramatists or biographers, ever did anything half so effective. The apostles are represented with weaknesses like our own, and yet at the end of any of the gospels not only is their Master more real to us than they are, but nearer to us, and more lovable. He is the most lovable human being of whom we have any knowledge. He is the wisest, the kindest, the most gracious. Not merely Christians alone feel this, but the great Oriental religionists as well. They may reject Christianity as Christians have made and stated it; but their wise men freely acknowledge the beauty of the Man behind it. Even the Jews, who have suffered so much at the hands of Christians, and through so many centuries, that the very name of Jesus might easily be to them a hateful one, are beginning to see in Him a great and loving Teacher. If you ask me if I believe in miracles I can only reply that this triumph on the part of ignorant and unlearned men is the very first miracle of all; and it is beyond question or dispute."

Though Bobby had followed this with his old-time manner of hanging on his father's words, he seemed to dismiss it when he spoke. "Yes, but I mean the miracles the New Testament says that Jesus worked. How could anyone feed five thousand men with five loaves and two small fishes?"

"To my mind," Leroy answered, choosing his words carefully, "it's not first of all a question of how He did it but of Jesus Himself. As a personality He has made the most profound impression on the human race that anyone has ever made. Buddha, Confucius, Mohammed have had vast armies of followers who've believed in their teachings; but I don't think any of them—though in this I speak at a venture and not with real information—I don't think any of them has endeared himself to humanity as Jesus has. When I used to go to church I often noticed that if the sermon was about an abstract subject like honesty or honour, or about Moses, or David, or Isaiah, some of the people looked bored, and some shaded their eyes and dozed. But the minute it turned on Jesus Christ everybody sat up and listened with all his attention. It would seem as if we could never hear enough about Him. Even when the preacher went over the same old ground with which we'd long been familiar we'd listen just the same. There is something about Him so winning, or that appeals so strongly to our curiosity, that He captivates us without fail. More than that, He captivates all ranks and classes equally. The poor and illiterate can understand Him as easily as the scholarly and the rich. In a certain sense they understand Him better, since He was their first great champion. But what I mean is that this personality, with His universal charm, is inseparable from what is told us of His so-called miracles. Mutilate the portrait and you cannot have anything

but a maimed, disfigured Jesus to contemplate
in your mind or to treasure in your heart. When
I think of abandoning what some people like
to call these wonder tales that's the first thought
that occurs to me."

Bobby asked bluntly: "And what's the second?"

"I think the second is that we in our generation should be the last who ever lived to deny
possibilities. It's on the ground of possibility
or impossibility that we generally believe in
the New Testament miracles or reject them.
The word 'miracle' itself is perfectly noncom-
mittal. It means simply something wonderful,
though there is an implication of something
admirable as well, since the root of the word
is the same as that of our word 'admire.' 'Some
strange good work,' might not be a bad definition; and we who live in an era of strange good
works should hesitate, I think, to disbelieve
that any strange good work, however impossible it seems, is wholly out of the question."

"I don't know what you mean by strange

good works," Bobby returned, in some perplexity.

"No, I don't suppose you do. You're too
young to have seen them done. Even the latest
of our modern wonders you can only take for
granted. But you'll see others. Wait a few years,
and things that would now seem utterly incred-
ible to you will be taken as commonplaces by
your children."

Bobby was eager for particulars. "But,
Father, what will they be?"

"How do I know what they'll be? I can't
foresee them any more than my father could
have foreseen the radio or my grandfather the
automobile. I wonder if you realize how miraculous these things would have been to them.
Very few of us realize how miraculous our
whole modern civilization looks by the side of
that of the great-grandparents of people of the
age of your mother and me, and we're not precisely patriarchal. You might say that these
miracles began on the night when James Watt
watched the kettle boil and started to think of

the motive power of steam. Up to that minute
there had been scarcely any scientific advance
since the time of Aristotle and Archimedes.
When Napoleon fought his battles not much
more than a hundred years ago he moved from
country to country very much as Julius Cæsar
did. Then began a century of miracles which
do not seem miracles at all to you, but do to
me and to most of my generation, and I'm only
thirty-eight. To my father, as I've already
hinted, they would have been astounding. I
remember how he used to laugh at the idea of
horseless carriages; and here we are with two
motor cars in our own garage. You've always
driven in a motor car; but your mother and I
haven't. The first time we ever did we didn't
get over the wonder of it for days. I've always
used the telephone; but I've heard my father
tell of the first time he spoke over it, and the
sense of the miraculous which haunted him till
he had one put into his own house. Your mother
and I felt the same thing only a few years ago
when we first heard by radio a concert given
in New York. You, who had been used to won-

ders all your life, were just too young to be astonished by one more. Just think of the things that electricity alone is doing for us. When my father built this house we had no light but that of smelly oil lamps, with candles in our bedrooms."

"Gee!" Bobby exclaimed, in the new language he had been learning to speak at school.

"And I remember the delight with which I came home one evening, when I was a little older than you are now, to find the whole house brilliant with electric light. I got out of bed in the night just for the pleasure of turning it on and off. Now electricity not only lights our house, but feeds our range, washes our clothes and irons them, takes the place of ice in our refrigerator, and does a lot of other things from toasting the bread at breakfast to curling your mother's hair. These may not seem wonderful to you, but to us——"

"Yes, but Chris," Mabel interrupted, "we know how all these things are done. They're done through material discovery and invention, and can be explained. But a miracle such

as Bobby asks about is performed by some un-
explainable process, and that's why we question it."

"Because you take no account of the fact that
nature is a vast storehouse of powers secret to
us, of which we've discovered a dozen or two,
while we easily infer that there are thousands
and thousands still to be discovered by future
generations. Now that the method is more or
less known there need be no end to it. Bobby
has just asked me what he and his children
should be enjoying which we as yet are not, and
I've told him I didn't know. For aught I can
tell scientists still unborn may supply him before he dies with a pair of airplane slippers
with which he will walk in the air, or a wireless invention that he can carry in his waistcoat
pocket, and by which he will call up anyone
in any quarter of the globe more easily than he
can now call up Susie or Peter on the telephone. I don't know. All I can say is that if
the eternal storehouse that we've tapped goes
on yielding up its treasures we need not be
astonished at anything."

"Yes," Mabel objected, "but that would still be what I've said, something we understand and can explain. Whereas a miracle such as we read of in the Bible——"

"I'm coming to that. What we don't know as yet, but what we're getting just an inkling of, is the unity of what we call the material and what we call the spiritual. Rather, it begins to look as if there were no material, but that everything is spirit or force or electricity or something equally intangible. Matter used to be our great reality. You could see it, touch it, eat it, stand on it, break it, build it. Now our scientists tell us that it is nothing but an agglomeration of atoms, and that atoms are but an agglomeration of particles of force to which they've given the names of electrons and protons, and which can be neither seen, nor heard, nor touched, nor perceived by any of our senses. In other words 'proton' and 'electron' are merely conventional expressions to express what is inexpressible, because there is nothing we can call material. That we don't call it spiritual either is, I believe, chiefly because scientists are afraid of the word. But the truth is that between matter and spirit the difference is growing very tenuous, and it is not the spirit that shows signs of giving way. Havelock Ellis puts it very well in his recent book, *The Dance of Life,* and if you'll wait a minute I'll read you what he says."

He made his way into the library, coming back presently with a volume in his hand of which he turned the pages. Switching on an electric light against the wall, and standing under it, he said, while he continued to hunt for the place: "For Bobby's sake I ought to explain that Havelock Ellis is one of the profoundest thinkers we have writing in English at the present day. Ah, here it is! It's quite short and bears directly on what I have to say about the miracles. 'Matter,' he read slowly, 'as psychologically-minded philosophers have at last begun to point out, is merely a substance we have ourselves invented to account for our sensations. We see, we touch, we hear, we smell, and by a brilliant synthetic effort of imagination we put together all those sensations and picture to ourselves "matter" as being the source of them. Science itself is now purging "matter" of its complicated metaphysical properties. That "matter," the nature of which Dr. Johnson, as Boswell tells us, thought he had settled by "striking his foot with mighty force against a large stone," is coming to be regarded as merely an electric emanation. We now accept even that transmutation of the elements of which the alchemists dreamed. . . . So that "matter" becomes almost as "ethereal" as "spirit," and indeed scarcely distinguishable from "spirit." ' Now listen specially to this. 'The spontaneous affirmation of the mystic that he lives in the spiritual world here and now will then be, in other words, merely the same affirmation as the man of science has more laboriously reached.' "

Switching off the light, he came and sat down again, taking a few puffs at his nearly extinct cigar to keep it alight. "Now I don't suppose that Bobby understands very clearly what that means——"

"I'm sure I don't," Mabel confessed frankly.

"Well, then, I'll explain it. It's only another way of saying, but on great authority, what I've just been trying to tell you. If modern science is correct we live primarily not in a material world but in one which I think we're quite at liberty to call spiritual. Scientists may avoid that word for the reason that they do not know what spirit is; but for people like ourselves, who are not scientists, and not bound to express ourselves in exact scientific terms, spiritual is as good a word as any. What we call matter, our bones and flesh, the ground we tread on, the house we live in, the food we eat, is an invention of our own to account for our sensations. It could all be dissolved, if we knew how to do it—which some day we may—into the electron and the proton, or in other words into the primal force which as far as we've discovered is the only true substance. From that it could be resolved back again, if we knew how to do it—which some day we may—into bones and flesh, the ground we tread on, the house we live in, the food we eat. It's a question of mentality or spirituality, express it as you please."

"All the same," Mabel reasoned, "I don't quite see what that has to do with the New Testament miracles."

"Do you see, Bobby?"

After faltering and stammering, the boy said shyly: "You mean that Jesus knew already what we're only finding out now."

Leroy was not only radiant but proud. "Good! You couldn't have expressed it better. He knew what the man of science is only reaching laboriously. Apparently He could dissolve the material back into primal force, and resolve the primal force back again into the material. Bobby asked me how He fed the multitude with the loaves and fishes, and I presume it was in some such way as that. How He could do it we have no idea; but then we don't know how He knew letters, never having learned. We don't know how He got His knowledge of the world or His power of reading the human heart. He didn't know scientifically, of course; He knew spiritually. He knew by constant reflection on God, the Source of all things, and on His own coöperation with God. He knew that

in whatever He wanted to do God would co-
operate with Him. He could not apparently
do all things with equal ease; but the more
difficult they were the higher His faith rose
to meet the situation. The best example of that
I can think of is in His calling Lazarus back
to life. Lazarus, as you know, had been four
days in the grave. To re-summon a spirit which
must, as it seems to us, already have travelled
so far away, was a stupendous thing for even
Him to attempt. But from the minute of hearing of the death He has no hesitation. He is
in Galilee, but He proceeds at once to Jerusalem. Bobby, give me that New Testament
again, and we shall see just how He was af-
fected." Bobby having handed him the version into modern speech, Leroy found the
place and read: " 'On His arrival Jesus found
that Lazarus had already been four days in
the tomb. Bethany was near Jerusalem, the distance being a little less than two miles. And a
considerable number of the Jews were with
Martha and Mary, having come to express

sympathy with them on the death of their brother. Martha, however, as soon as she heard the tidings, Jesus is coming, went to meet him. "Master, if you had been here," she said, "my brother would not have died; and even now I know that whatever you ask God for, God will give you." ' "

Turning a page, Leroy resumed his reading, a little farther on in the passage. " 'Mary, when she came to Jesus, fell at His feet and exclaimed: "Master, if you had been here my brother would not have died." Seeing her weeping aloud, and the Jews weeping who had come with her, Jesus, curbing the strong emotion of His spirit, though deeply troubled, asked: "Where have you laid him?" "Master, come and see," was their reply. Jesus wept silently. . . . Again restraining his strong feeling He came to the tomb. It was a cave, and a stone had been laid at the mouth of it. Jesus said: "Take away the stone." So they removed the stone.' "

Leroy allowed the book to rest on his knee,

while he called their attention to what he was
going to read next. "Now this is the critical
passage, giving us the clue to His whole attitude toward God, as well as the proof of what
He says elsewhere about prayer. He was asking of God support in the most difficult thing
any man had as yet ever undertaken. Moreover, it was in some ways an unreasonable
thing, and in others a superfluous thing. Lazarus had been four days in his grave and would
one day have to return there. Why disturb
him? Since he had died and the first shock to
his sisters had already passed, why not let death
have its way? But I think our Lord persists in
it simply to show us what man in coöperation
with God is equal to. Now observe that He had
not as yet done anything. Lazarus was still in
the tomb, as they could see, wrapped round
and round with graveclothes. Nevertheless—" he began to read again—" 'Jesus lifted
up His eyes, and said: "Father, I thank Thee
that Thou hast heard me; but I know that Thou
always hearest me." ' " He closed the book.
"That is," he went on, "before He had risked

His reputation in those mighty words, 'Lazarus, come out!' He knew that there would be a response to them, because of God's coöperation. Whatever He decided to do—unreasonable, superfluous, though it might be—God would support Him according to the measure of His faith. He knew that the task was terrific, that the risk He was running could easily be fatal; but He knew too that His faith was strong enough, and that God would not fail Him."

"Still," Mabel reasoned pensively, "I don't see that you explain the upset to all our natural laws that miracles like these would bring about."

"How do you know they would? That used to be an argument against them, but I understand that scientific men have given it up on the sheer ground that we know so little about natural laws. What we have called natural laws are now recognized as simply a succession of observed phenomena which we haven't been able to observe very far. There was a time when scientific men were very fond of seeing a law in everything they recorded. Now they're chary of coming to that conclusion, with the result that the more they learn the less they know they know. Where a generation ago we talked of Darwin and Huxley we now pin our faith to Freud and William James. That is, we're coming to recognize the superiority of mind, and its power over everything else; but, once more to call Havelock Ellis to our aid, Jesus knew already what we only work out laboriously."

Bobby raised another point. "But if He knew so much why didn't *He* give us the telephone, and the motor car, and the radio, and everything? I should think He could have, as easily as not."

"I haven't the least doubt that He could," Leroy answered promptly; "but He gave people what they needed first and most. In their little country and with their very simple way of living their wants were much more basic. Ravaged by the most terrible diseases, leprosy, palsy, eye-troubles, insanity which they called possession of the devil, their chief need was of healing, and He gave them that. Poor and idle because of Roman oppression and the lack of employment, they needed food, and He gave them that. Hopeless and yet with a capacity for hope beyond that of any other race, they needed a national outlook, and He gave them that. They would have had no use at all for a car or a radio set; but they did know when they were healed and fed and inspired."

Somewhere at a distance a clock struck ten. "My gracious!" Mabel cried, "it's ten o'clock and, Bobby, you know you should have gone to bed at half-past nine."

"Forgive him for this time," his father pleaded. "His holidays are nearly up. But I should like to add just this, that I haven't the slightest wish to urge a belief in the miracles on those who find it difficult; but I do think that living in such a storehouse of wonders as our present world we should hold our judgment in suspense, and keep an open mind."

Dutifully Bobby got up and kissed his

mother good-night; but when he passed his father he slipped his arm over his shoulder with a little squeeze, a caress which Leroy knew that he would think of in his heart for a long time to come.

CHAPTER VIII

WHAT IS THE FORGIVENESS OF SINS?

IT WAS still another Bobby who came home
for Christmas, a subdued, pensive Bobby, subject to fits of abstraction, and wearing a hang-
dog look. Mabel wondered what could be the
matter; even Ellie, who was now ten, asked
her brother what the trouble was; but the father
was pretty sure he knew.

Bobby's birthday being in February he was
now nearing fifteen. At thirty-eight Leroy had
still a memory of that age so keen and fresh as
to infuse into his affection an element of yearning. Knowing what the boy was facing, he
would gladly have saved him from it, while
aware that there was no way of doing it. He
himself had not been saved from it; his father
before him had not been saved from it; so
you could go back from son to father and from

177

son to father till you lost yourself in the obscurity of primitive men; and always you would find the ever recurring cycle of curiosity, desire, temptation, and sin.

He recalled his own anguished state of mind when that ugly word "Sin" first began to have for him an actual significance. He was about the age at which Bobby was now, and the scene was also the Doolittle School. Hitherto sin had meant smoking a cigarette in the privacy of Uncle Charlie's stable, with his cousin Tom, who had since then become the father of Bobby's second cousin Peter; swearing back at Tom when Tom had sworn at him; making an excuse which would not have borne investigation, though he tried his best never to lie directly. And then, one day something happened, after which the world was changed for him. He knew now what it was to eat of the Tree of the Knowledge of Good and Evil. Smoking a forbidden cigarette, or swearing at Tom, or being guilty of a lie that was half a truth, had only made him uneasy; this set him frantic. Frantic was the word. He never again heard or read the third chapter of what some people called the Book of Beginnings without understanding what Primitive Man and Primitive Woman had felt on the realization that they had eaten of that Tree—the mad rushing about to hide themselves; the covering themselves up from each other's eyes; the stammering confessions; the dreadful sense that innocence was of the past, and that an angel with a flaming sword kept them from finding the way back again. It expressed exactly what he himself had felt, though outwardly he went on with his lessons, observed the rules of the school, and conducted himself as if nothing had happened to his inner man. He grew silent, sullen, aloof, till at last a fellow older than himself—now a well-known banker in Boston—chaffed him on his churlishness.

He was what Leroy called a "nice fellow," and though some years older than himself they often chummed together, discussing athletics, politics, or, as boys sometimes will, the big eternities of life and death. One day when they were doing the last Leroy, whose heart was full to bursting, blurted out his confession. But the "nice fellow" only laughed at it. He even mimicked Leroy's tone of repentance. "Oh, yes! never again—till the next time. We all make that good resolution, and keep it in that way—never again—till the next time. You'll get over it."

This laughing, cynical tone made Leroy's struggle for the next few years not a little harder. It surprised, comforted, and weakened him all at once to know that in his sin he was not alone. He had thought of himself as branded like a Cain; and to learn that nearly every other fellow—even a "nice fellow" like this chap from Boston—could be branded too did much to diminish his sense of guilt. The next time! Was it possible that in spite of all he had suffered during the last few weeks there was going to be a next time? A sermon he heard in the school chapel did something to suggest that there would be. It was to the effect that we were not to be discouraged when we had fallen into sin if we had tried with all our

might to keep out of it—that God gave credit
for the effort even when it did not end in success. So that should there be a next time . . .

A few months earlier he had been confirmed,
and with his mother had two or three times
received the Holy Communion. That these
means of grace had not saved him in advance
was one of the reasons why he began to question their efficaciousness. Then it came to him
that perhaps he had not striven enough on his
own account, and so he prayed for help. This
he kept up till he perceived that in his inner-
most heart he was hoping that the help would
not be given him, or that it would not be strong
enough. By getting sufficient credit for the
fight he was putting up he would also secure
his forgiveness when he fell—the next time.
The game was such a double one that it became distinctly a relief when, in his second
year at college, he forsook the Christian system altogether, and so freed himself from
these ruses to deceive his own conscience and
cheat God. It was a dark period in his life, and
continued into his early manhood. By that

time, however, he had grown as callous as the nice young fellow from Boston, and could take it all with a laugh.

It was the third day after Christmas, and to please Ellie the Christmas tree had been lighted up for the last time. Next day it was to be dismantled and taken away. Even Bobby felt some regret that a year must go by before they could have the festive, many-coloured thing again. With their father at the piano and supporting them with his strong baritone, Bobby's boy treble and Ellie's childish soprano rang out together in some of those old English carols which preserve the lusty Christmas spirit in a way which the more subjective, sentimental American ones do not. "God rest you, merry gentlemen"; "A Virgin unspotted"; "Good Christian men rejoice," made an excellent reproduction of the quaint old English waits, till Mabel bustled in and sent Ellie to her governess for supper. She had come from a piano recital where she had met neighbours who lived near them in summer time.

"And did you know," she asked her husband,

while giving him such scraps of news as she had picked up, "that both of those Smeaton brothers, the florists at Kidlington, had committed suicide?"

Chris replied that he had known it, but had said nothing about it because the story was so ugly.

"What made it ugly?" Bobby asked, with a boy's curiosity.

Leroy threw some significance into his reply. "I was told that they had got into bad habits as boys, and so went on from bad to worse till they took to drugs. They always lived together, and what one did the other did. When the elder, desperate in his fight against drugs, committed suicide, his brother followed his example the next week. It's not a pretty story, so I didn't mean to say anything about it."

"They were always queer," Mabel commented, "but they grew the most lovely flowers. Now let's all go and dress for dinner. Don't let anyone be late because we are having a cheese soufflé, and if it's kept waiting it falls."

At dinner Bobby was silent, with the silence

of meditation. Not till they were all three seated in the library did he give a hint of what was in his mind.

"Do people commit suicide because they think they're so awful bad?"

"Some do, I believe," Leroy answered him. "I doubt if it's the motive very often. When it is it seems to me largely a matter of not understanding the principle behind the forgiveness of sins."

"But, Father," Bobby cried, as if he were in trouble, "what *is* the forgiveness of sins? How can you get it?—and what good does it do you when you do get it?"

Leroy took time to think. "Before I can answer that," he said, weighing his words, "we must understand as nearly as we can what sin is."

"I thought everyone understood that," Mabel threw off coolly.

"Well, what is it, then?"

"It's some form of immorality, isn't it?—I mean immorality in the broad sense, not in the narrow."

"You might put it in that way," Leroy agreed, thoughtfully. "To me it's simply the wrong way of doing things. It's an injury done to ourselves which makes it harder to reach God."

Mabel, who had been idly turning the pages of an illustrated paper, let it drop on her knees while she said: "Say that again, Chris, will you?"

He repeated his definition.

"That," she commented earnestly, "is the queerest idea of sin I've ever heard expressed."

"Because you believe in the stool-pigeon God, which is the ideal of most Christians."

The nature of a stool pigeon had to be explained to Bobby. He was an individual who, knowing your weaknesses, decoyed you into them, and then betrayed you to the police, acted as witness against you, and had you put in jail.

Leroy again addressed his wife. "You've believed that God created us with all sorts of desires, made them as necessary to us as breathing, watched to see if we would gratify one of them, and when we did flew into a passion of anger and saw to it that we were punished. If He couldn't contrive to punish us in this world He had many ingenious tortures in the next."

"That may be it," Mabel admitted, "put crudely."

"Put it in any way you like and you'll never find a more misleading travesty of the God who is called the Father by Jesus Christ. The stool pigeon is the meanest creature on earth, more crooked than the crookedest of crooks; and that's what we good people have made of a God who is a fountain of tenderness and generosity."

"Well, Father," Bobby questioned, "how is it that He does give us all these temptations to do things that we oughtn't to do——?"

"But He doesn't, Bobby; He never has. The stool-pigeon God is merely a mischievous tradition come down to us from people who misread the Bible—especially the Old Testament —three and four and five generations ago, and largely, I'm sorry to say, right here in America. What God has always declared Himself to be is a God of Righteousness; and when I say that

He has so declared Himself I mean that thoughtful men long ago perceived that He must be so. Now what do we mean by righteousness? Most people limit the word to the purely moral righteousness of not robbing our neighbour, killing him, or bearing false witness against him. I don't. To me righteousness is a much bigger thing than that. I should define it as the right way of doing anything. I should apply it to every item in our lives, to work, to society, to art, to sport, as well as to religion. A God of Righteousness is simply a God of the Best Results. That being right, thinking right and doing right produce the best results is a matter of course. On the other hand, being wrong, thinking wrong, and doing wrong must in the long run end in disaster. This reasoning is so simple that even when men were still primitive they could understand that a God such as He whom they were beginning dimly to descry must love the right way of doing things and hate the wrong. 'I, the Lord, love righteousness,' are the words somebody puts into His mouth, 'and hate iniquity.' Naturally enough! because iniquity, any kind of tackling life in the wrong way, must react injuriously on the man whom God loves."

"All the same," Mabel argued, "you wouldn't say that a man who had failed in business, let us say, was guilty of unrighteousness."

"The application of principles to individual cases is not exactly the job for us. We know too little of each other. We are too poorly equipped for passing judgment. Of the man who fails in business we can say that he must have made mistakes, and mistake after all is essentially what sin is. The difference, of course, is that his error is in temporal things, while sin is mistake in the spiritual. More often than not sin is the attempt to get good results— or results that at the time appear to us to be good—by a mistaken method. Then any kind of evil, chiefly in the sinner's person and career, can be the consequence. We speak of sinning against God—and of course the phrase is quite legitimate—when we really mean sinning against ourselves. God is not the victim of my wrongdoing, but I myself am. From that there is no escape till I turn from the wrong way of doing things to the right one. Even then some lingering effects of the wrong may continue to dog me, but by doing right in the main my results must in the main be good."

"Well, then," Bobby said thoughtfully, "sin isn't so terrible after all."

"Oh, yes, it is, because it destroys our capacity for making the best of life; and we hardly ever realize that the best of life is identified with God. It is God manifested in us and through us, and sin interferes with the process. It is not that God is no longer there; it is that sin keeps us from making use of Him. It's like a cataract on the eyes, a veil which comes down over our spiritual vision. People who commit a great many sins, and do so with an easy conscience, get so spiritually atrophied that God is not a reality to them any more."

Bobby having asked the meaning of the word "atrophied" understood it easily.

"That's the worst of forming a bad habit," Leroy threw off, as if speaking casually. "We

never know how soon it's going to fasten itself
on us, till we either become indifferent to God,
like a majority, perhaps, of the people of the
world, or desperate because of our loss of Him,
like the two Smeaton brothers at Kidlington.
In any case, sin being the wrong way of doing
things, brings on us all sorts of evil conditions.
Even primeval man understood this, for he
knew that in the day when he ate of the Tree
of Knowledge of Good and Evil he would
surely die. That is, already in the mind of man,
in the far-off prehistoric ages which could only
be summed up for us in legend, a connection
between sin and destruction, between sin and
death, was more or less established. It was also
more or less established that God had no need
to punish sin, because sin punishes itself. It's
true that the ancient phraseology of the Old
Testament, and sometimes of the New, speaks
as if God were always on the alert with some
form of chastisement; but we must interpret
that in the light of what we have since been
given to understand of Him. What primitive
man saw dimly became more and more a cer-

tainty as his knowledge of God increased. Possibly the most sublime expression of this attitude of God toward sin and the sinner is given in the first chapter of Isaiah. Just listen while I read you a few lines of it."

As he put out his hand to pick up the Bible lying on his desk Bobby intercepted him. "Let me find it," he begged, beginning to turn the pages. "What does it come after, Father?"

Leroy replied that he wasn't sure, but he knew it was further on than the First and Second Books of Chronicles. Bobby continued to fumble till at last he exclaimed, "Oh, here it is: Isaiah, Chapter One," reseating himself as his father began to read.

" 'Hear, O heavens, and give ear, O earth, for the Lord hath spoken. I have nourished and brought up children, and they have rebelled against me. The ox knoweth his owner, and the ass his master's crib; but Israel doth not know, my people doth not consider. Ah, sinful nation! a people laden with iniquity! a seed of evil doers! children that are corrupters! They have forsaken the Lord; they have provoked the Holy One of Israel to anger.'"

Leroy let the book rest on his knee while he exlained that this was the sort of language used by the prophets, taking, as it were, the words from the mouth of God in order to dramatize their messages. But it was the pleading with which the passage concluded that was the more highly indicative of God's position with regard to sin. Tersely and yet vividly it set before the mind the good results of the right way of doing things and the evil results of the wrong way.

"'Come now, and let us reason together, saith the Lord. Though your sins be as scarlet, they shall be as white as snow; though they be red like crimson, they shall be as wool. If ye be willing and obedient, ye shall eat the good of the land; but if ye refuse and rebel, ye shall be devoured with the sword; for the mouth of the Lord hath spoken it.'"

Mabel spoke pensively. "The language is magnificent, and yet as fact——"

"As fact it entirely disproves the theory of the stool-pigeon God which we Christians, both Protestants and Catholics, have so long persisted in. And yet there is another passage which does it with greater beauty still." He passed the volume to his son. "Bobby, find me the One Hundred and Third Psalm."

Very inexpertly and with much turning of the pages now to one end of the Bible, now to the other, Bobby lighted by accident on the place.

"This to me," Leroy said, before beginning to read, "is one of the most inspired lyrics we can find in all literature, ancient or modern. You must read it for yourselves. I can give you only the lines that bear directly on what we're talking of. 'He hath not dealt with us after our sins, nor rewarded us according to our iniquities. Look how high the heaven is in comparison with the earth—' that is," Leroy interjected, "infinitely high—'so great is His mercy also toward them that fear Him. Look how wide the east is from the west—' infinitely wide—'so far hath He set our sins from us. Yea, like as a father pitieth his own children even so is the Lord merciful unto them that fear Him. For He knoweth whereof we are made; He remembereth that we are but dust.' Not much of the stool-pigeon God about that, is there?" he concluded, with a smile.

The silence which followed was broken by Mabel with a question. "But doesn't that seem to minimize the guilt of sin—rather?"

"It might if it was all we had on the subject. If we're under the impression you speak of there is plenty to correct it. Perhaps our Lord's way of treating sin does more than anything else to clarify our minds on that point. Except now and then when He heaps up His invective against hypocrites and hypocrisy—the sin He seems to have detested most—or looks round about Him with anger at insincerity and cowardice, He allows Himself neither the fierce denunciation of sin, nor the pleading with the sinner to give it up, which marked the ancient prophets. He is content to trace effect to cause, somewhat in the manner of the Freudian psycho-analysis of the present day, and to leave the victim of sin to draw his own conclusions. When they bring to Him a man sick of the

palsy, lying on a stretcher, He does not say to
Him: 'Yes, you're in this condition because
you've been a great sinner.' Seeing their faith,
He says, simply: 'Son, be of good cheer; thy
sins be forgiven thee.' Of Mary Magdalen He
says: 'Her sins which are many are forgiven,
because she loved much.' To an impotent man
whom He had healed He says: 'Sin no more,
lest a worse thing come unto thee.' Of the
woman taken in adultery He asks: 'Woman,
where are thine accusers? Hath no man condemned thee?' She said,' No man, Lord.' And
Jesus said unto her, 'Neither do I condemn
thee. Go and sin no more.' That seems to me
to indicate clearly enough the stand He takes,
and therefore to give us an idea of God's own
attitude. Sin is the wrong way of doing things,
bringing with it all sorts of ills, not excepting
physical ones. The easiest way of escaping the
ills is to give up the sin. If we can't give it up
altogether we escape in proportion as we do
give it up. No effort on our part, however
small, loses its reward. That's what I mean by
the principle behind forgiveness."

"But forgiveness doesn't do away with physical ills, does it? Very good people are often very great sufferers."

"I think that must depend on our command of spiritual power, which at the best is small. Even Jesus didn't heal every sick person with whom He came into contact. He healed only those who approached Him with a measure of faith, and the permanence of their healing seems to have been a matter of their not sinning any more. It isn't merely that He forgives us; we help to forgive ourselves by taking the right way instead of persisting in the wrong. With our present weaknesses healings are often no more than partial. But healings don't cover everything. To revert to the right way of doing things may help us in many ways, even when we continue to suffer in the flesh."

Mabel seemed to consider this, saying after an interval of silence: "I'm not sure that I know what forgiveness is—exactly."

"I'm not sure that I do either," Leroy replied, "beyond what the word itself implies. Did you ever notice how it is made up? It's simply our everyday word 'give' with the Anglo-Saxon prefix *for*—which makes for intensification. That is, forgiveness is to give richly, royally, with might and main. It's something offered spontaneously and graciously. It's one of the most appealing exercises of Divine Power because it's called forth by our weaknesses. How the coiners of language reached this truth is a mystery. But not only did they do it, but they did it very generally. We get precisely the same thought in the similar word 'pardon.' This, of course, we take from the French *pardonner,* which is also an intensification of *donner,* to give. The German word *vergeben* is of course but the equivalent of our own, and serves to show that even among the wild Teutonic tribes the idea was indigenous. Forgiveness seems to be God's largest, most liberal, and most loving gift to man, closely connected with the life and death of Jesus Christ, and beyond that there's little we can say about it."

Mabel spoke only after some reflection. "That seems to me rather noble."

"It's not only rather noble, but the conclusion Jesus Christ drew from it is nobler still. To be in a condition to receive God's pardon we must stand ready to pardon others. It's forgive us our trespasses in proportion as we forgive those who trespass against us. By this I think He must mean not only the forgiveness of big injuries done to us—which after all come only now and then if they come at all—but all the little foolish irritations which meet us every day in the home, the school, the office, the drawing room, any of the gathering places where human beings come together. People have their foibles, but don't notice them; they have their meannesses, but don't notice them; they have their evil tongues, but don't notice them. Freely ye have received, our Lord says, freely give. I think we may add to His words and make them, freely *for*-give too."

Bobby's voice had a kind of wail in it. "But, Father, can't I be forgiven unless I forgive those who trespass against *me?*"

Leroy knew that they were close to the heart of the boy's trouble. "I don't see why you should be an exception. Were you thinking of anyone in particular?"

Bobby hesitated at telling tales out of school, but the crisis was unusual. "There's a fellow at the Doolittle who did something awful mean to me just before the holidays began. I told him I'd fix him after we got back. I know I can and not give him any chance to squeal. And don't you think I might settle him first and forgive him afterward?"

"That I should have to leave to you. It would depend, I should think, on how much you feel the need of forgiveness for yourself."

Bobby lapsed into reverie, broken only by the words spoken less to his father and mother than to his own conscience:

"Well, I guess I'll leave him alone."

CHAPTER IX

WHAT IS THE RESURRECTION OF THE DEAD?

IT WAS Easter morning. Bobby and Ellie stood at the window of the front drawing room, watching the people streaming into the church across the street. Their mother in a dressing gown of soft black silky stuff, embroidered to the knee in irises, mauve, purple, yellow, red, with plenty of green foliage, perched on the arm of a big chair, keeping out of sight from the crowd below. The weather being balmy, the windows were open, while the peal of the organ rolled up to them triumphantly. As the church was what is known as a fashionable one, Mabel was interested in picking out now this friend and now that, and noting what they "had on."

"Mummy, what's Easter," Ellie demanded, "and why does everyone have to have a new hat?"

Mabel had heard that the new hat was the last mild trace of the spring Bacchanalia of the ancients, but she thought that Ellie would do as well without that information. Into the more spiritual significance of the festival she could not trust herself to go.

"I'd rather you asked your father that, darling. He'll explain to you."

"I can tell her," Bobby volunteered. "We read all about it in the Bible two or three days ago. We always have Bible lesson, only we just read it. Nobody tells us what it means the way Father does."

Concisely but correctly Bobby told his sister the story of the Passion, Crucifixion, the Resurrection, scarcely having ended when a hymn was wafted over from the church.

"Jesus Christ is risen to-day; Alleluia!
Our triumphant holy day; Alleluia!
Who did once upon the Cross
Suffer to redeem our loss;
    Alleluia!"

"Mummy, why don't we ever go to church?" Ellie questioned, when the hymn had ceased.

"Well, we never have," the mother replied, as if that were an explanation. "Besides, when I've gone I've always had a choky feeling, as if I was going to strangle."

Naming a number of her little playmates who went every Sunday, Ellie said that one of them had told her that there would be a children's flower service in the afternoon. "Couldn't I go to that, Mummy?"

"If your father would take you—yes, dear."

"I'll take her," Bobby spoke up. "I know how. You just go in and sit down."

So it was settled, and they went, only to return in consternation and shame on Bobby's part. It seemed that the chancel had been decorated with pots of flowers which were distributed among the children of the Sunday school. When they trooped up to receive these rewards of merit Ellie slipped from the pew and pushed her way among them. Under false pretenses she had received a pot of geranium bearing one small, sickly, salmon-coloured

flower. Ellie loved it; but Bobby, hot and red over her audacity, declared he would never take her anywhere again. When, however, on this announcement Ellie wept aloud he felt that in the spirit of his father's teaching, which ever since Christmas he had been trying to put into practice, he must forgive her, making her promise to be more careful for the future.

For the rest of the day it seemed as if this had been his only impression of the service; but when they were all gathered that evening in the library, and Ellie had gone to bed, he produced another.

"Father, there was a man talked in the church this afternoon who said there would be a day when Jesus and His angels would come out of the sky and someone would blow a trumpet. Then all the people who were dead and buried would come out of their graves, and meet their fathers and mothers and families, who'd been dead and buried too, and all be united again. But—" he frowned in perplexity —"I don't see how that could be, do you?"

Leroy, who was standing near one of the

bookcases, ran his hand along a row of volumes. "Every one of these is on that subject. I've read them all, and I don't know that I'm much the wiser. The Christian religion brings up a good many questions hard to answer, and this one seems to me the hardest. It's the hardest because it has to do with a future which of our own experience we don't know anything about."

It was not, however, one of the subjects on which he had "read up" for Bobby's sake. Having done not a little of the latter, he found his interest in religion for itself growing deeper and more sincere. As an intelligent man, reaching the time of life when the more serious aspect of things begins to occupy the mind, he was becoming aware of a vital concern for his country, for its social conditions, for the welfare of men in general. Incapable of the easy optimism, and still less of the *laisser aller* indifference, of so many Americans, he was somewhat desperately looking for a principle, or a set of principles, on which he could base a reasonable hope. This he hadn't found; and yet of one thing he grew more and more convinced, that if in this passion-torn world there was anything like a saving inspiration it sprang somewhere from the teaching of Jesus. The question was how. That teaching had been before the world for two thousand years, and yet it had not forestalled the most terrible catastrophe that had ever overtaken the human race. The churches had all been on the side of their fellow countrymen, of whatever nation. Protestant had slain Protestant, Catholic had slain Catholic, the brotherhood of faith counting for nothing at all. God had been the God of the national arms of each, as Dagon was to the Philistines, Moloch to the Syrians, and Jehovah to the Hebrews. Even the voice of the One Strong Church, or what was left of it, could not make itself heard above the thunder of the firing lines.

"I must find out for myelf," Leroy said then; so he took to reading. He read discursively, and reflected. He reflected chiefly with a view to simplification. Whenever he turned to the churches for aid what he got struck him either

as beside the mark, or as over-elaborate. It was
never, it seemed to him, the exact teaching of
Jesus Christ. It was the teaching developed
from that teaching by Greeks and Romans who
had twisted and shaped it to suit their fancies
or ambitions for over a thousand years. When
out of the womb of the One Strong Church had
sprung its progeny of Protestants—disowned,
it was true, but all the same its progeny—German, Swiss, Scandinavian, Scotch, American,
and what not, the confusion of leadership
compelled him to fall back on books.

For a year now he had, on and off, been
studying this question of a Resurrection. By
this he meant not so much the Resurrection of
Jesus as that which the majority of Christians
believed to be somehow awaiting mankind.
Finding to his surprise a fairly generous literature on the subject, he bought and read everything in English on which he could lay his
hand. So he had worked out an understanding
that for aught he knew might be wholly unor-
thodox and untheological, but which in a measure satisfied himself.

"If you like," he said to Bobby now, "and if it won't bore your mother, I'll explain the little that I know about how the ideas you heard this afternoon came to be so generally held."

While Bobby curled himself up in an armchair in order to listen with greater ease, Mabel protested that she would not be bored. Leroy spoke as he leaned on the low bookcase.

"I think what strikes me most is the reticence of the Bible, both the Old and the New Testaments, on the subject of a future life of any kind. Not that it is ignored; it is only treated with extreme reserve. You might read the whole of the Law and the Prophets, and still be unconvinced as to whether the Hebrews believed in a future life or not. A very good idea of their prevalent opinion can be found in the thanksgiving psalm, written by King Hezekiah after he had recovered from an illness which had brought him to the point of death." Picking up a Bible, he handed it to his son. "Bobby, find me the Book of Isaiah."

With some difficulty Bobby discovered it, after which his father found the chapter.

"Ah, here it is. I shall only read a few lines, but it will give us the gist of what even a good man at that time felt about death. 'I said in the cutting off of my days I shall go to the gates of the grave; I am deprived of the residue of my years. I shall not see the Lord in the land of the living. I shall behold man no more with the inhabitants of the world. . . . For the grave cannot praise thee; death cannot celebrate thee; they that go down into the pit cannot hope for thy truth. The living, the living, he shall praise thee as I do this day.' That," Leroy continued, "was as far as they had advanced even in times so enlightened as those of Isaiah. Death was the grave, and the grave was *Sheol* or 'the Pit.' At the hands of our English translators 'the Pit' becomes 'hell' or the 'hole,' the words being different forms of the same Anglo-Saxon root, meaning to hide something, to put it out of sight, as being too ghastly to look at. As to life after death this is as far as the Old Testament takes us, except for a few scattered hints."

Bobby was interested. "Tell us some of them."

"I don't know that I remember more than one or two, but they'll be enough to show us that though it didn't very often find its way into books there was a more highly developed hope on the part of the more spiritual." He turned to the Book of Psalms. "Here's one, for example. 'I have set the Lord always before me . . . therefore my heart is glad . . . my flesh also shall rest in hope. For thou wilt not leave my soul in hell, neither wilt thou suffer thine Holy One to see corruption. Thou wilt show me the path of life; in thy presence is the fulness of joy; at thy right hand there are pleasures for evermore.' Now without undertaking to say exactly what these words mean it does seem clear that they must apply to some happy state. The same thing is true of the concluding verse of the next Psalm, even though the thought is indefinite. 'As for me, I will behold thy face in righteousness. When I awake with thy likeness I shall be satisfied.'

With a few more such passages the Old Testament tells us all that it has to say about a future
life, till we come to its very latest book, that
which bears the name of Daniel. But before we
touch on that I want to say something else."

Taking down a volume from the shelves, he
turned the pages here and there as if to refresh
his memory. "What I've been telling you," he
went on once more, "refers only to what's
written. But people couldn't help thinking independently of that. They couldn't help new
ideas coming into their minds, nor could they
help it when, as so frequently happens, the
same ideas came to a good many people at the
same time. Since the ideas were in the air, they
couldn't help discussing them. There was
therefore a whole trend to public opinion of
which the Old Testament takes little if any
notice. Except for the Book of Daniel, there
is a gap of some four hundred years between
the Old Testament and the New; and in four
hundred years the outlook of the human mind
moves a good many stages farther on. It was
during that time that the subject of survival, of

judgment, of resurrection, of immortality, became an active preoccupation."

"I've often wondered," Mabel observed, "why they produced no literature in so long an interval."

"Oh, but they did—a very considerable literature. First there's the Book of Daniel, which dates from something like a hundred and sixty years before Christ. Then we have what to us are the ten or twelve books of the Old Testament Apocrypha—books we consider doubtful but which the Roman Church accepts as belonging to what are called the canonical Scriptures. Then there are a number of other books not so well known, but with which scholars are familiar. In all of them the subject which Bobby heard spoken of this afternoon is an ever-recurring theme. The end of the world, the future of the soul, the punishment of the wicked, the reward of the rightous, had for these generations the same kind of fascination that hairsplitting doctrinal definitions possessed for the earlier Christian centuries. Of this the only echo that comes from

the Old Testament is heard toward the end of
the book which goes by the name of Daniel."
Picking up the Bible again, he spoke as he
turned the pages. "After a series of visions
something like those in the Apocalypse the
writer begins his last chapter in this way: 'And
at that time shall Michael stand up, the great
prince which standeth for the children of thy
people. . . . And at that time thy people shall
be delivered, every one that shall be found
written in the book. *And many of them that
sleep in the dust of the earth shall awake,* some
to everlasting life, and some to shame and
everlasting contempt.' If you were better
acquainted with the Old Testament you would
see how different this is in thought and style
from everything that precedes it. That the idea
of a resurrection will be familiar to his readers
the author takes for granted."

"And was it familiar to them, Father?"

"By this time, I think, it must have been. So
much had been written about it, it had been
so generally discussed, that I don't believe there
could have been anyone who hadn't heard of

it. But it was not resurrection alone that was
in their minds; it was the whole question of
future rewards and punishments, and God's
judgment of the world. To that subject, too,
some of the prophets of the Old Testament,
especially the lesser ones, make a certain
amount of reference. There was to be what
they called a Day of the Lord, when the earth
was to tremble, the mountains fall, the seas dry
up, and the sky disappear, while anguish took
hold of the nations. It was all very grandiose,
and all very vague. But into it there enters no
suggestion of a resurrection. That came later,
and even when it came there was a good deal
of confusion as to those who should rise and
those who should not. Some declared that only
the righteous would do so; others that righteous
and wicked alike should come out of their
graves, some to blessedness, the rest to suffering. There was also a dispute as to whether or
not the Gentiles should share in this restoration, or only the Chosen People. But of all their
utterances on the subject the soberest and the
most reserved will be found, I think, in the

positive could be foretold. In fact, He takes occasion to say that of the day and hour of all this neither man nor angel nor He himself knows anything. His work is specially for the here and now."

"And yet," Mabel commented, "He Himself rose from the dead. You believe that, don't you—or do you?"

"Yes, I believe it, as I believe in what are called the miracles, because it completes the portrait. Without the Resurrection the picture we have of Him would be so distorted that it would no longer be His picture. Besides which I've no information whatever as to the limits to possibility. Even if I doubted the Resurrection I could never deny that it had taken place for the very good reason that I've no means of positively knowing that it didn't. Neither has anyone else. Our position with regard to it strikes me as very like His own with regard to Resurrection and Judgment. To assent to what is traditionally held, at least till we know enough to contradict it, seems to me the only reasonable course."

Leroy went on to say that the Resurrection of
Jesus differed essentially from what was popu-
larly known as "the general resurrection at the
Last Day." In the latter case the dead were
called out of their graves to meet an eternity
of bliss or woe. In the former a man overcame
the corruption of death by His spiritual knowledge and power. It was another instance, to
quote Havelock Ellis again, of the spiritual
man going straight to the point which science
reaches laboriously. That is, Jesus apparently
possessed by spiritual means that understanding of the nature of matter which science has
only discovered in the Twentieth Century, and
of which the majority of men and women are
still unconvinced. He knew that matter could
be analyzed back to force, and that what is
force to the physical scientist is spirit to the
man of God. He knew, as Havelock Ellis implies, that the material body was only an illusion created by man himself "to account for
his sensations." He knew that it was but a mistake of the senses, and that in reality it did not
exist. All that did exist was the spiritual man,

made in the image of God, and of that the senses could take no cognizance.

Over this spiritual body physical death could have no power. Its only power was over that body which, according to modern science, had in reality no existence. Death was therefore an illusion, just as the body it claimed to kill was an illusion. Strictly speaking, what is called the Resurrection of Jesus seemed to him not a resurrection at all. It was His withdrawal from the non-real into the spiritual reality, which is the only reality there is. At the same time He reserved the power, for the sake of those who were still under the domination of the senses, to bring Himself at times within their illusory limitations, so that they could know He was still "alive." When He did this He was emphatic in declaring that He was not a ghost. "A ghost," He said, "hath not flesh and bones as ye see me have." He breathed; He talked; on one occasion at least He ate in their company. He invited them to touch Him, so that they could see for themselves that in the sense which they considered real He was a reality. Having convinced them of this He passed into the real world altogether, whereupon they said that He "ascended" into heaven. As a matter of fact, Leroy found the word "ascension" as inexact as "resurrection," since the points of the compass could have had nothing to do with it. They used, however, the only terms they possessed "to account for their sensations."

"But," Mabel argued, "if the human body is only an illusion of the senses what about the end of the world and a general resurrection? How could there be a resurrection if there's no physical body to rise?"

"About the end of the world I've nothing to say. It's a question for the astronomers. But I think we must understand a general resurrection according to our present knowledge, and not according to pious speculations which we have outgrown. In this we're considerably helped by St. Paul, and all the more so because he appears to have undergone a development in his ideas which brings him by stages nearer our modern point of view. At first he seems to have acquiesced in the feeling which the early Christians held in common with the Jews and Greeks, that an immortality without the physical body would be hardly worth the having. All they knew of personality, whether their own or that of those they loved, was identified with that body. It was the cast of the features, the colour of the eyes, the tones of the voice, that made up the individual. These created reality, and must be restored to give reality to a future state. That in spite of death and decay there should be such a restoration had become in the course of generations a fixed belief, to be passed by the Jews to the earliest Christians, who passed it in turn to the first of the Gentiles to accept the faith. Moreover, it was a conviction on the part of most of these Christian groups that that resurrection should be soon, an expectation which St. Paul, at first at any rate, seems to have shared."

In the first of the epistles he ever wrote, Leroy explained further, considered to be the oldest of the books which now make up the New Testament, the First Epistle to the Thessalonians, he gives details as to how the resurrection was to take place which he would probably not have repeated later in his life. The Thessalonian converts were apparently distressed because some of their number had died and would therefore miss that return of the Lord which was so speedily to take place. The apostle writes to reassure them. "I would not have you ignorant concerning them that are asleep, that ye sorrow not as others which have no hope. For if we believe that Jesus died and rose again, even so them also that sleep in Jesus will God bring with Him. For this we say unto you . . . that we which are alive and remain unto the coming of the Lord shall not forestall them which are asleep. For the Lord Himself shall descend from heaven with a shout . . . and the dead in Christ shall rise first. Then we which are alive shall be caught up together with them in the clouds to meet the Lord in the air, and so shall we ever be with the Lord."

It was probable, Leroy went on, that during the years immediately following St. Paul heard so much of the resurrection of the material body that he was compelled to revise in a measure his own position. Writing some years later to his converts in Corinth he is careful to correct the stress which so many laid on the physical. "Now this I say, brethren, that flesh and blood cannot inherit the kingdom of God, neither doth corruption inherit corruption. . . . There is a natural body, and there is a spiritual body. . . . Howbeit that was not first which is spiritual, but that which is natural, and afterward that which is spiritual. The first man is of the earth, earthy; the second man is the Lord from heaven . . . and as we have borne the image of the earthy we shall also bear the image of the heavenly."

Bobby asked, with curiosity: "What would a spiritual body look like?"

"We've not the least idea. It's no use trying to imagine it. We talk about spirit, but we have no means of knowing what it consists of, or how it is perceived. All we know is that it cannot be detected by our senses. When the risen Jesus withdrew from the physical non-real into the spiritual reality mortal eyes could not follow Him. They said He had vanished, when what really happened was that their own powers of sight had become inadequate. But there's one thing of which we can feel assured; if there is this spiritual body it's a body more substantial, more powerfully built, and better adapted to its purposes than the one we've got. This mortal illusion which we call the flesh is ingenious, elaborate, and makes a great show of being skilfully put together, but there's always something wrong with it. As a bit of machinery it's a bungling piece of work, always needing, from the cradle to the grave, to be patched up in one part or another. A good deal of it is sickening, and within a few days after death it becomes loathsome. To me it's a relief to have science come and tell me that it's only a creation of our own, since I can thus acquit God of ever having made it."

"But did He make the spiritual body any better, Father?"

"We can only presume He did. As far as our knowledge goes, which is not very far, the spiritual man is the man in the image of God. I know that it's the traditional belief that this mortal body is the man in the image of God, but a God with legs and arms and digestive organs like our own is not conceivable. Nobody could think that 'this corruption,' as St. Paul calls it, is man in the image of God who hadn't first made for Himself a God in the image of man."

But Mabel and Bobby would see, Leroy continued, that the man who had written what St. Paul had said to the Corinthians had travelled far beyond the somewhat naïve description, probably taken verbatim from the school of the rabbis at Tarsus, given to the Thessalonians. And yet some years later we find him at a point further advanced still. In one of his most beautiful epistles, that to the Colossians, written not very long before his death, we find him speaking of the resurrection as an inner spiritual experience belonging to the here and now. Not, of course, that he would limit it to that, but it has that aspect among others.

"He tells these Colossians that their conversion to Christ has been a veritable resurrection from the dead. 'Buried with Him in your baptism,' he read from his modern translation, 'you were also raised with Him. . . . To you, dead as you once were in your transgressions . . . He has nevertheless given life. . . . If, however, you have risen with Christ seek the things that are above, where Christ is. . . . For you have died, and your life is hidden with Christ in God.' That is," Leroy went on, "whatever we may feel as to a future opening of the graves, with the gathering of the myriads of the dead to be condemned or acquitted like the accused in some supernal law court, this constant renewal of life in Christ can be a daily experience. And there, I think, we must leave it. To insist on fuller detail would be, with most of us, to ask more than we can receive. This does not mean that highly sensitized minds, like Sir Oliver Lodge, Sir William Barrett, or William James, men of great attainments in other fields, should not be allowed to make their investigations without petty cavil on our parts; but those of us who have no such equipment do well, as I've said already, to wait, to trust, and keep the open mind. With a subject on which the imagination can so easily be set aflame perhaps the less we say the better. I shouldn't talk about it now only that Bobby has already heard it discussed this afternoon, and once a year we have Easter to keep it in our minds. But I feel very strongly that with the little that we know none of us can dogmatize. To me it's enough to feel, with the author of the Book of Wisdom, that 'the souls of the righteous are in the hand of God'; only I should go a short step further and add, 'and the souls of the unrighteous, too.' "

CHAPTER X

WHAT IS HUMAN BROTHERHOOD?

LIKE everybody else Mabel had her worries
and anxieties. In her immediate family, with
Chris and the two children, she was comparatively free from them; but when she turned to
her own relatives there was scarcely one who
did not present a problem. Of her sisters,
Gladys had divorced her husband, while Clarice's husband had divorced her. Though each
had found a second husband, there was no telling how soon another scandal would be sprung.
Her elder brother, Jack, was frankly a ne'er-
do-well, and was living in the Philippines;
Ned, the younger, was a lawyer in the city,
having much ado to make a living. The war
had unnerved him but had left him the legacy
of a penniless English wife, who in her turn
had blessed him with four children of whom

three were alive and thriving. To keep three children thriving and alive was becoming, for a young man of no inherited means and a limited earning capacity, a more and more difficult task, given American conditions.

Mabel liked Susie, her English sister-in-law, notwithstanding the suspicion that she had taken Ned not so much for love as because the supply of Englishmen had so tragically given out. Of good country family, Susie had not the aptitudes that make for expatriation. To her neat suburban home, with its three bathrooms, its electric outfit, and scant accommodations for "help," she brought the traditions of Flamborough Park, where the servants were so many that the small fry waited on the great ones, while only the great ones waited on the "masters." She could never get used to the idea that the cook didn't need a kitchen maid to bring her tea and bread and butter before she got up in the morning, or that the door could be properly "answered" or the meals correctly served without the supervision of a butler. Nevertheless, she took her situation bravely, learning to do such portions of the work as there was no one else to do, and striving to keep out of debt.

Devoted to Ned as Ned was to her, Mabel did what she could for his little family. All the clothes, hats, shoes, and toys which Bobby and Ellie had outgrown were passed on to the children, while she scrimped on her personal allowance to make them little gifts in cash. As to this, however, she was uneasy, as Chris himself never did anything of the kind. Chris, Mabel had noted long ago, was generous with money where he deemed it should be spent, but he never spent anything he could reasonably save. Beyond a five-dollar bill at Christmas to each of his young relatives on Mabel's side, he interested himself little, either in their parents or in them.

For this reason Mabel did not take him deeply into her confidence when Ned and Susie were called on to face what to them was a calamity. The landlord having raised the rent above anything they could pay, they were forced to look for a cheaper house. This meant a cheaper neighbourhood, with the contacts that implied. It would also involve a break with the little church which Susie loved and in which she headed the Altar Guild, finding in its sweet activities a link with her old home. All through the spring Mabel had taken her motor car to drive Susie about on what is in American life the most disheartening of all quests. Occasionally when, in the evening, Chris asked her what she had been doing in the afternoon, she mentioned the fact that she had been house-hunting with Susie, but as he never questioned further she told him nothing more.

By the time she was obliged to move to their house in the country Susie had discovered nothing. Mabel spent the summer, therefore, with a somewhat heavy heart, till just before their return to town Susie called on the telephone to say that they were not after all to be forced to move since a fairy tale had come true. Mabel understood her to say something about this being due to herself and that Susie was eager to see her to express her thanks, but as there was a buzz in the receiver the exact words escaped her. So long, however, as she knew that they were not to be obliged to move she did not insist on fuller details.

With her first free hours on returning to the house in town she drove out to see Susie. What she heard then amazed her more than anything she could remember during all her married life. If it made her happy it also made her grave, silent, pensive. To Chris she said nothing till the confidential hour after dinner. The evening being chilly, a fire had been lighted in the drawing room, where they sat Darby-and-Joan-wise, one on each side of it. Mabel had her work stand, which she didn't touch. Chris read a book, of which she had already seen that the title was, *What Is Human Brotherhood?* Across the back drawing room she could see into a corner of the library where Bobby, deep in a great leather armchair, was engrossed in a tale of the gold rush in the Klondike.

"Chris, you're awfully queer," Mabel said, at last. "Do you know it?"

He allowed the book to drop to his knee,

though marking the page with his finger. "I'd begun to suspect it; but how have you come to find out?"

"I've been to see Susie."

He shifted in his chair uneasily. "Oh?"

"And she says you've bought that house and deeded it to her."

"She's told you that, has she? I was hoping she wouldn't say anything about it."

"The idea! Of course she would. She tried to tell me over the telephone two weeks ago, and I didn't understand her. Naturally, I know you must have done it for my sake, and I can't tell you how——"

"Oh, but, darling, I didn't—or only indirectly. Except in so far as you're the link between Ned and Susie and me you'd have had nothing to do with it."

Mabel swallowed a little disappointment. "But I didn't know you cared so much about them."

"I don't. They're all right. I like them, in a way, but they're not the kind I should ever have picked out——" He broke off to correct himself. "This is the way I should put it. Till I bought that house and made it over to them I didn't really care anything about them, beyond the fact that they belonged to you. Now——"

As he hesitated she supplied the phrase. "You like them a little better."

He spoke thoughtfully. "Liking isn't the word. It's rather a kind of—of tenderness—such as you feel toward children when you're looking after them. But that came later. When I did the thing it wasn't from affection for anyone."

Mabel looked her amazement. "Then for mercy's sake, Chris, what could have been your motive?"

"That's a little difficult to explain. I'll see if I can tell you."

While he reflected Bobby strolled from the library toward the fire, asking as he perched on an arm of his father's chair: "May I listen, Father?" Consent being given, he put a hand on his father's knee, while the latter flung an arm over the boy's shoulder.

"You see the title of this book?" As he held it up Bobby read the title aloud. "Well, the subject has been in my mind all summer. It was after our talk about the Resurrection last Easter Day that it first began to force itself. I was thinking of the hold which this teaching of the Resurrection had taken on the mind of the Apostolic Age, and I wondered why. I still wonder why, because as we see things in the Twentieth Century it has not, I think, the most forcible kind of appeal to us. Mind you, I'm far from saying that the Apostolic Age was wrong while we're right; I'm only noting the difference in our point of view. The resurrection of the dead is too far away, too problematical, for us to dwell much upon it in the pressure of things more immediate. Not that it wouldn't always be a theme of commanding interest, only that I don't think any of our churches, or bishops, or popes would make it the touchstone of Christian teaching if we were beginning again."

"Well, what would they make the touchstone, Father?"

"That's the very question I asked myself. I said, What other principles did they have which we at the present day would consider more forceful, more urgent, than that of the Resurrection? And I thought of two. The first I've spoken of long ago. It was the Kingdom of Heaven. As far as I could judge that had been abandoned shortly after the Apostolic Age. At least I could find no emphasis laid upon it till it began to be identified with the Church, and the Church to be identified with a powerful hierarchy and an elaborate system of doctrines and rites. The more the history of the Church developed the more it seemed to me to become a Church of the Kingdoms of This World and the Glory of Them, and the Kingdom of Heaven to be blotted out. That was the first thing."

Bobby's questions were generally to the point. "And what was the other? You said there were two."

"The other was not so much taught by Jesus as it was implied in everything He did. He doesn't always teach directly; He implants a principle and lets it work. He never, for example, says a word against slavery, though slavery was one of the most cruel institutions of His time. But no one could even remotely be His follower without seeing it was wrong. In the same way I don't remember that He ever expresses in so many words the idea of the brotherhood of man; but no one can be familiar with His life without getting it by implication. That His disciples had fully grasped the principle of brotherhood we can see from their first attempt at social organization, which was on a basis of brotherhood unknown in the previous history of our race. 'Neither said any man that aught of the things which he possessed was his own; but they had all things common. . . . Neither was there any among them that lacked; for as many as were possessors of lands or houses sold them, and . . . distribution was made unto every man according as he had need.' "

"Well, why don't we do that now?" Bobby demanded eagerly. "Then everybody would have plenty, and nobody would have to work."

Leroy smiled. "That's just the point. The apostles seem to have found that in a world such as they had then there were too many people who would take advantage of this generosity, and that it couldn't be kept up. We should probably find the same in a world such as we have now. But that it remains the Christian ideal when we can carry it out, which will probably not be for another two thousand years, is a fact, I think, that we cannot get away from."

Mabel suggested that the failure of the first experiment might have been the reason why the apostles didn't emphasize this brotherhood more explicitly in their preachings.

Chris admitted that this might be so. "But," he continued, "all the same it remains one of the most original ideas, and one of the most appealing, ever set before the human race. When it can be put into practice mankind will have approximately reached the standard of Jesus Christ."

"Yes, *when!*" Mabel sighed. "But there's nothing that looks like it now, is there? I suppose there never were so many bitter enmities as there are at the present minute."

"That's the way I used to think," Chris agreed with her. "It seemed to me there could be no such thing as human brotherhood till all the world, or a good part of the world, got together and worked out a plan. Unless it were on something like a colossal scale it didn't seem to me as if it could be brotherhood. Other people, that is to say, were to be brothers to me before I could act as a brother to them. In fact, for a good many years of my life I've been hung up right there."

"And, Father, what cut you down?"

"I wasn't cut down at all; I was lowered by degrees. First it came to me that if there was to be a brotherhood of man it was, so to speak, to begin with me. I mean that I was the only brother for whom I was responsible. I'd been looking for kings and bishops and saints to start the ball rolling, when it was my job to start it for myself. In other words, the brotherhood of man begins with the individual. Till he acts there can be no brotherhood."

"And yet," Mabel said thoughtfully, "it's a good deal for one individual to undertake—to be brother to the whole human race."

"That was where I was stuck next. Willing as I was, or fairly willing, to put the idea into operation, as far as lay in my power, I didn't see how I was to be a brother to the Russian, the German, theAfghan, the Englishman, the Irishman, all at once. I felt that unless the scale of the brotherhood was vast it couldn't keep up with the immensity of the requirements. I saw no way of practising brotherhood till we got a great many others to practise it too. If the whole conception hadn't haunted me I should have given it up."

"I can't see," Mabel observed again, "why you didn't give it up, as it was."

"Because one day when I was fumbling about in the New Testament I lighted on that part where St. John asks if a man doesn't love his brother whom he has seen, how *can* he love God whom he hasn't seen? Well, there was the whole thing in a nutshell. It so clearly made my relationship to God dependent on my at-

titude toward men that it almost scared me.
My next step was to try to discover who was
meant by my brother."

"But you haven't got a brother," Bobby
cried, presenting a difficulty.

"No; but that was only my second thought.
My first was that my brother must of necessity
be *my brother*—the son of my father and
mother—the being of my own flesh and blood.
And, as Bobby says, I had none. I had no sister, either. I had you two, and Ellie, and that,
I said to myself, was all. If brotherhood had to
begin at home then I had satisfied the condition, since I loved the three of you."

"And wasn't that enough?" Bobby asked.

"It wasn't enough, because if brotherhood
begins at home it's part of the conception that
it cannot end there, otherwise it wouldn't be
brotherhood. To be effective it must extend
to the person next, and then to the person next,
and then to the person next, till it takes one
farther and farther. No one individual can go
very far, but each should go as far as his oppor-

tunities carry him. I remember once, when I was a big fellow of eighteen or so, I was camping out with some other chaps in Maine. And we started what might have been a bad forest fire if we hadn't managed to put it out. To cook our breakfast we'd made a fire in an open space, not terribly far from the ring of trees, and yet, as we thought, far enough to be safe. We got through our breakfast all right, and had packed for moving again. The fire had to all appearances gone out, though to be quite sure about it one of the crowd kicked an ember, meaning to stamp on it. But before he could do that a cloud of sparks flew up and a low branch of a spruce tree was on fire. Then the one above it was on fire; then the one above that; then the one above that. Presently all the inner side of the tree was ablaze, each branch passing on the flame to the one above it. Well, somewhat in that way I think the spirit of brotherhood should go, to the next, to the next, and to the next, as far as the individual's capacity will take him."

Mabel had been considering. "And Ned and Susie came next after the children and me. Was that the way you reasoned?"

"That was the way I had to reason. Having no brother or sister of my own I naturally thought of yours."

"With a view to buying them the house?"

"No; not with a view to anything in particular, except to show myself friendly. The first time I went to see them we said nothing about the house, though I knew from you that they were going to move, and why. That, I considered, was something for them to swing, and took for granted that they could. The second time——"

"Oh, you went to see them twice."

"I went every time in August when I ran up to town on business."

Mabel reckoned. "That was four times."

"Yes, four times. And it wasn't till the third that I'd got what I called a challenge."

"A challenge? From anything Ned or Susie said?"

"No, from something I said to myself. I'd

been trying to show my sense of brotherhood by the cheap and easy method of looking in on them. And when I saw what the real need was I was up against it. Here was a call to do something, and I didn't want to *do* anything. You may have noticed that I'm not an easy spender, except in the way of adding to our own luxuries. I'll confess to you now that for two or three days I was mean enough to be sorry I had not let Ned and Susie alone, and so know nothing about them beyond what you had told me. As it was I didn't find out what the trouble was from them, but from a chap at the club— that friend of theirs, Billy Frobisher—who told me that they had either to buy the house or pay half as much again in rent. Challenge was the word. I saw that I should have to go ahead and do the thing, or give up the principle of brotherhood for shame. So I went ahead."

"But, Chris, it must have meant such a lot of money—forty or fifty thousand at least."

"As a matter of fact it was forty-five; but what's that to us? I've been through all the arguments with myself, and know that we can

very well afford it. At first, it did seem a stag-
gering sum to spend on other people, but when
I thought it all over I could see that neither
you nor Bobby nor Ellie would ever have to
go without a new pair of shoes or a ticket to the
theatre for lack of it. The good Lord blessed
me with a fair-sized personal estate from my
father, together with the dominant interest in
a highly successful business, which Uncle
Charlie's good management has made more
successful still. All the same it did seem a good-
ish amount; but now that I've put the deal
through it gives me more pleasure than anything I've ever done before."

"To me," Mabel said, with awe in her voice,
"it's the most wonderfully generous thing I
ever heard of."

"Oh, no, it isn't. Think of the sums people
no better off than I am give to hospitals, to
colleges, to art galleries, to institutions of all
kinds. They give their money into the air, as
it were, without seeing or knowing the individuals who are to profit by what they do. I
know Ned and Susie, and get all the satisfac-

tion of their pleasure and relief. That makes it so much the easier for me. And now I might as well tell you that I've done something else."

"In the way of spending money?"

"No; money won't be a question in these instances. I've been to see Gladys and her husband, and also to see Clarice and hers. I called on them both last week. I didn't see either of the men, but I found both your sisters at home."

Mabel leaned forward, tense with repressed excitement. "What *could* have been your idea, Chris, in doing that?"

"I didn't have any idea beyond what I had in going to see Ned and Susie. I wanted to show myself friendly. I wanted to imply that you were friendly too, and I think I gave that impression. Gladys was a little stiff, but Clarice cried and sent you her love."

"But, Chris, I don't see them any more. I don't even write to them. After the way they've got themselves talked about, and in the newspapers too——"

"Did you ever wonder why the good Lord, in bringing us into the world, placed every one of us in a little family? Wasn't it that we should stand shoulder to shoulder and back to back? When I was a small boy, and for my soul's good learned the catechism, we were taught that the Ten Commandments were divided into two parts. The first four gave us what we called our duty toward God; the remaining six our duty toward man. And our duty toward man began with the family. We were to stand by our fathers and mothers, and presumably our brothers and sisters too, if we were to live long in the land, which was the ancient way of expressing the idea of success. All our duties, all our kindnesses, all our forgivenesses, were to spring, as it were, from the cradle."

"Yes, but, Chris, it's often a great deal harder to get on with your relatives than with anybody else. I've never pretended to hit it off with Gladys and Clarice. Ned and I have hung together, but we're the only two of the whole lot of us who have. And yet, as a matter of fact, it's on your account that I've stopped having anything to do with the two girls. I didn't want you to feel yourself tied up with people you couldn't help being ashamed of."

"Darling, I appreciate that; but it's in the past. Now what I should like you to do is to ask the whole four of them to dinner."

Mabel was troubled and surprised. "Together?"

"That was my idea."

"Oh, but I don't believe they'd like it. Gladys is as down on Clarice as I've ever been." She remembered now that this might not be the kind of talk best suited to the ears of a boy. "Bobby, you'd better run back to the library and read your book."

"No, let him stay," his father begged. "He's as much a member of the family as we are, and will soon have to take his own stand with regard to its problems. If Gladys doesn't want to meet Clarice she needn't come. What we've got to do is to give her the opportunity. I believe she'll be glad of it. Anyhow, the point for us is to show ourselves well disposed toward the lot of them, and let things work out as they will."

Mabel considered this. "How would it do to ask Ned and Susie too?"

"It would be so much the better."

"Susie, of course, might be difficult; but now that you've done what you have for *them* I should think that her heart might be softened."

"It's a matter of all our hearts. We shall feel freer and more unburdened once we've come to be on better terms with each other. It will help me especially, because if I feel easy in my mind with regard to the family—that is, if I feel that I've done my best there—I can go a little farther afield. In the factory, for example; there are fellows there, good fellows too, and some of our head men, who have to work together, and yet hate each other like poison. Well, with a very little effort on my part I could get them to understand each other better. I've seen that for a long time, and have been too lazy or too indifferent to make a move. Now I should like to——" Allowing his sentence to hang up there he stared at the fire and mused. "And there's another thing," he began at last. "I'm going back to a church again. I wouldn't do it if I didn't feel obliged to, but I do. I don't agree with the churches, not with any of them wholly. But that no longer seems to be the point. Feeble and cranky and preposterous as you can make them out to be, they do represent our chief agency for good. My job, it seems to me now, is not to be over-critical of what others are attempting, but to do the little that I can to help. It's easy to look on and jeer, as I've done for twenty years and more, but that doesn't get us anywhere."

"And when you say help," Mabel asked, "what exactly do you mean?"

"I haven't the least idea. I suppose that by keeping my eyes open I could find out. If there's nothing else, it will be something at least, I presume, if I can do what I'm trying with Gladys and Clarice and their husbands, just show myself friendly."

Mabel made her suggestion timidly. "Couldn't I show myself friendly too?"

He flashed a smile at her. "Darling, of course! I didn't want to make the suggestion; but now that you've made it yourself——"

Once more his voice trailed off into a silence, broken only when, after long meditation, Bobby asked:

"Father, isn't that kind of brotherhood something like the Kingdom of Heaven?"

"I think it is, old boy. I'm not sure if the best way of finding the Kingdom of Heaven for ourselves isn't in trying to bring it to somebody else."

"I know," Mabel interposed, "that there's something in the Bible about laying up treasure in heaven; only that that always seems to me such a long way off."

"Oh, but I don't think it is," Leroy corrected. "Our Lord's heaven was here and now. That's why He was so much preoccupied with the present. When He speaks of treasure on earth and treasure in heaven I don't think He means a local earth or a local heaven of any kind. His reference is to a state of mind and heart. In telling the rich young man who wanted to be perfect to sell all he had and give to the poor— which simply means to let others share in the good fortune so liberally given him—and he would have treasure in heaven, I'm sure He was thinking of blessedness in this life before it was blessedness in any other. I've a strong conviction that if He is our Saviour He's our Saviour now; and that if He's our Saviour now it's to save us from undue ills of whatever kind at the moment which we're living through. But if He's to save us we must do something to save ourselves; and perhaps we best save ourselves by helping to save our brother first. So that you'd be perfectly right, old chap. George Eliot says somewhere that the Kingdom of Heaven is within us as a great yearning. I used to think that a very fine phrase, and often repeated it; but now I see that it doesn't mean anything. It's true that the Kingdom of Heaven is within us, but as an impulse to do things, and especially to do things for others, and find our happiness in that. Do you remember that a long time ago I gave you the definition of religion as the tie which binds the world together, man to God, and God to man, and men to each other?"

Bobby said that he remembered it.

"Well, then, doesn't brotherhood work that definition out? It seems to me that we do a lot of worrying about God—as to who God is, and what He is, and whether there's a God at all—which we should escape if we did more worrying about men. To love the brother whom we have seen is the surest method of loving the God whom we have not seen. Our Lord says something of the same kind when He tells those who have loved Him without knowing it: 'Inasmuch as ye have done it unto one of the least of these, *my brethren,* ye have done it unto Me.' In other words God appears before us in the form of man. Serve man and you will be serving God. And in your service of man begin at home."

To this the only response was a silent one, but because of its silence all the more deeply felt. Though Mabel and Bobby looked into the heart of the fire, each felt the glow of a more enduring flame, while Chris returned to his book.

THE END